THE ILLUSTRATED BOOK OF
WILD ANIMALS

Text *by* WILLIAM BRIDGES

Curator of Publications, New York Zoological Park

Based on
WILD ANIMALS OF THE WORLD

GARDEN CITY BOOKS, GARDEN CITY, N. Y.

OF THE WORLD

Animal Portraits by MARY BAKER

Introduction by ROY CHAPMAN ANDREWS

Copyright, 1948, by

DUENEWALD PRINTING CORPORATION

LITHOGRAPHED IN THE UNITED STATES OF AMERICA
IN 1960

MAN IS not the only animal with curiosity, but he is the only one who writes, publishes and buys books to satisfy his itch for knowing. And among his books, since the very earliest days when there were books, have been books about animals — the wild animals that share the world with him.

Since the fifteenth century it is probable that millions of copies of books about animals have been bought by people who never saw, never even hoped to see, the animals they were reading about. Pure curiosity about the wild animal life must have prompted a vast amount of that reading through the ages.

The Illustrated Book of Wild Animals of the World is an attempt to satisfy the curiosity that is so prevalent today. "Conservation" is a new and important word that we are hearing more and more often; it is, indeed, the most important word in our language. For it has come to mean the saving, and the rebuilding, and the wise usage, of the natural world on which our very lives ultimately depend.

Wild animals are a vital part of that natural world. They, like ourselves, are dependent upon it for their lives and well-being; they, like us, modify it and change it by the very fact of their existence. Their good, and ours, sometimes conflict; more often, probably, if we but knew more about the interaction of all natural forces, we would find that animal interest and ours coincide.

The point I am making is that today, more than ever before, our human curiosity about the sub-human creatures of the earth is more than pointless curiosity; whether we know it or not, our lives are affected by the wild animal population of the world. Thus it is important for us to know a little more than most of us do about those animal friends and enemies.

The Illustrated Book of Wild Animals of the World is not written from the Conservation viewpoint, although there are occasional references to the fact that such and such an animal is of economic importance. It aims at the broader plan of furnishing factual biographies of the representative mammals of the world — thereby, we hope, serving that generalized curiosity that is the starting point for more specialized interests.

The biographies in this book are concerned with 172 best-known mammals, the ones that are most likely to be talked about in books of African adventure, or seen in the great zoological gardens.

W. B.

INTRODUCTION

WHEN I FIRST looked at Mary Lee Baker's superb paintings I wondered how she had been so successful in catching the subtle charm of a wild thing that makes a portrait, a sketch or word picture true and impressive. Then I discovered that she paints to music.

"I must have complete relaxation," she says, "so I select four or five recordings of symphonies such as Brahms', Mozart's or Beethoven's. I work in absolute quiet except for the music and the emotional and mental balance that results helps me to forget time and place and to almost live with the animal I am painting."

That interested me enormously. When I was Director of the American Museum of Natural History we tested the effect of music in the Akeley African Hall where great habitat groups have brought Africa to New York. Recordings of soft music, the throb of tom-toms and native instruments were played over a broadcast system with immediate success. Visitors sat on the benches in front of different groups completely relaxed, seeing Africa, hearing Africa and feeling Africa. Seldom did one move except to walk quietly to the next exhibit.

Miss Baker has another interesting work habit. She finds the complete quiet of very early morning most conducive to concentration and repose and begins painting shortly after midnight. For two years she has worked on the illustrations for this book and the results show it has been a labor of love.

William Bridges is responsible for the animal biographies. No one could be better equipped to select and tell about the animals most interesting to the public. Newspaper work gave him training in popular writing and taught him how to present facts of natural history in palatable form.

"While I was working as a reporter on the New York *Sun*," he says, "I made two or three trips a year to the New York Zoo because I have always loved animals. The place was literally crawling with good feature stories. Eventually the Zoo became my regular Monday assignment. Then I was sent to cover an expedition of the late Dr. Raymond Ditmars to Trinidad to capture a bushmaster, the most deadly of all the great poisonous snakes of the Western Hemisphere. Dr. Ditmars got the snake and I got some wonderful stories, which later became my first book, *A Snake Hunter's Holiday*. I liked newspaper work but animals were my passion and in 1935 I was given a new job, title: Curator of Publications of the New York Zoological Park.

"It has been quite a few years since 1935 and I still pinch myself now and then to see if it is real. I can't imagine any work that would be as varied, as exciting, or that I would love as much. It has taken me all over the world and every day has been one to dream about.

"In the summer of 1946, the Zoological Society sent me to the Belgian Congo to act as their representative in accepting and shipping three young African elephants, presented by the Belgian Congo government to the Society. Afterwards I spent five weeks touring the Belgian Congo by plane, automobile and afoot to gather material and stories.

"Writing this book has been great fun for even such condensed accounts of the lives and habits of animals revive vivid and unforgettable memories.

"I remember a sweaty, dusty Australian aborigine limping home from a hunting expedition with a tuckered-out dingo riding across his shoulder . . . A polar bear stalking a man across the Arctic snowfields . . . A sloth bear asleep in the hot sun on a hillside in Ceylon.

"These and hundreds of other scenes and incidents crowd in my mind. What a panorama the animal life of this world presents! If *The Illustrated Book of Wild Animals of the World* informs and awakens interest in natural history in its readers it will have done its work well."

Thus the authors have told, in their own words, their background for doing the book. It is a good equipment and the job is a good job. Perhaps their most difficult task was the selection of what animals to portray. There are approximately fifteen thousand species and subspecies of mammals in the world. Obviously, not all of them could be described. Had it been possible, it would have been undesirable, for many species differ so slightly that only a scientist could tell they were different. Even though one gorilla is a little larger and its hair is thicker than the other, it is still a gorilla with the same general habits and characteristics. So only one gorilla has been portrayed. But we have two elephants, because the Asiatic and African elephants are quite unlike in appearance and habits. Moreover, one is likely to find both in any big zoo. The authors' choice of material has been largely based upon the mammals one can see in zoos or read about most frequently in books of travel, sport and adventure.

Although *The Illustrated Book of Wild Animals of the World* isn't complete in a technical sense, therein lies one of its many virtues. It is a practical and comprehensive guide book to the world of mammals with a wise elimination of confusing details which would be of interest only to the scientist.

More and better zoos are being established in American cities because people want to know about animals. Millions of dollars and the thought of eminent men in every walk of life are expended in bringing the animals of our own country and foreign lands to those who cannot travel. *The Illustrated Book of Wild Animals of the World,* with its beautiful portraits and authoritative descriptions is a zoo which can be taken even into the home.

ROY CHAPMAN ANDREWS

"AARDVARK" is a Boer Dutch word that means "Earth Pig." The animal's plump, yellowish-brown body, covered with sparse grayish-brown hairs, actually looks pig-like, but it is not a pig; indeed, the Aardvark has the distinction of belonging to a zoological order, family and genus all by itself.

Its home is in East and South Africa. By day it sleeps, curled in a tight ball with its snout tucked under its body, in a deep hole. After dark it comes out to feast on the termites whose mounds dot the forests and plains by the millions. Often these mounds of sun-hardened mud are so hard that a stout man can scarcely hack into them with a bush knife, but the Aardvark manages to tear them apart with its claws, and as the soft-bodied termites emerge from their honeycomb of cells, the animal licks them up with its long, sticky tongue.

It can run surprisingly fast, for such a heavy-bodied animal, and if it is cornered it rears up, supporting its weight on its hind legs and tail very much like a kangaroo, and delivers slashing blows with its foreclaws.

An adult Aardvark weighs about one hundred pounds. As a destroyer of termites it is a useful animal, and is given a certain amount of protection in some parts of Africa. Meat-hungry natives seldom heed the game laws, however.

ADDAX

AFRICA is the home of most of the antelopes of the world and in that vast continent there are antelopes that fit into almost every kind of country. Some live in thick and humid forests, some on the grassy plains, some on the rocky and sandy deserts.

The Addax is one of the desert-dwelling antelopes and ranges from Senegal to Egypt. It is medium-sized, standing about three and one-half feet high at the shoulder, and it has a beautiful pair of brown, spiral horns that are ringed for the greater part of their length. Only the males of some antelopes have horns, but both the male and the female Addax have them.

Like so many animals that dwell on the desert, the Addax can go many days without drinking. It is a shy and wary creature and extremely fleet of foot. In the old days, the Bedouins or tribesmen of the desert used to chase the Addax to test the speed of their horses, for they knew if they could overtake this fleet animal their horses were very fine ones.

The Addax has a thick mane on its neck and shoulders in winter. The mane is brown and the rest of the animal is covered with short, yellowish-white hair. Across its face is a band of white hair that makes it look as if it were wearing a bandage.

RODENTS, or gnawing animals, form the largest order of mammals and they are particularly plentiful in South America. The Agouti is one of the best known, for it lives well in captivity and is usually to be seen in collections of Central and South American mammals.

This smooth-coated little animal has olive, golden-brown or reddish hair. An adult may be eighteen to twenty inches long.

The Agouti is usually found in thick forests where it hides during its resting hours in burrows among the roots of a tree, or in a hollow tree. Leaves, roots and fallen nuts or fruits are its principal food and hunters have learned a trick of throwing a stone into the leafy branches of a tree to call the Agouti out of hiding. Apparently the Agouti hears the noise of the falling stone, thinks it is a fruit or nut that has fallen, and comes to investigate — whereupon the hunter gets a shot. The flesh of the Agouti is very good eating.

It is a swift runner, making a series of hops and springs almost like a gallop. When pursued by dogs, it readily takes to the water and it can swim well, although it does not seem to know how to dive.

There are more than a dozen kinds of Agoutis.

ANOA

THE SMALLEST of the world's wild cattle is the Anoa that lives on the island of Celebes in the Dutch East Indies. It is only about three feet three inches high at the shoulder; another name for it is the "Pigmy Buffalo." To most of us, "cattle" denotes the placid cow, but there is nothing placid about this member of the wild cattle family. It has horns twelve to fifteen inches long and it knows how to use them — as one American zoological garden learned to its cost. It quartered a newly-arrived Anoa in a compound next to a highly-prized muskox. Within five minutes, the Anoa had dealt the musk-ox such vicious jabs through the wire fence that the musk-ox died.

Young Anoas are thickly covered with light brown, woolly hair that tends to disappear as they grow older. Old adults are sometimes completely bare, but their hide is so tough that it is reported to be immune to the blood-sucking land leeches that are such a pest in the Celebes.

Man is the Anoa's chief enemy, for its flesh is very good eating, and the hide is much prized by natives because it makes a strong, white, tough leather.

The horns of the cow Anoa are always smaller than those of the male. In its tropical home in the Dutch East Indies, the animal shows that it is truly one of the cattle family by its fondness for standing or lying in the shade, often in a pond or in a muddy creek.

QUITE UNLIKE the Giant Anteater and the tamandua in appearance is their relative, the Silky Anteater of tropical America. It is a tiny creature — its head and body are only about six inches long, its tail seven or eight inches — yet it is a savage fighter.

If it happens to be asleep in the daytime, curled up in a tight ball on some small limb, any unusual jostling of the limb will cause it to uncurl and rise up to its full length, holding on by its hind feet and its tail and waving its long-clawed forefeet menacingly. Let an enemy get too close, and instantly the foreclaws make a slashing stroke. Oddly enough, the Anteater pays no attention at all to the shaking and dipping of its branch caused by the wind.

The Silky Anteater's tail is as good as an extra hand, for it is strongly prehensile. Holding on with hind feet and tail, it can extend its body sideways from a limb to grasp another leaf or branch, and not until its new foothold is secure does it let go with the tail.

It is nocturnal, sleeping among the leaves in the daytime, roaming at night in search of the termites that are most active after dark. These it flicks up with its sticky, worm-like tongue. The Silky Anteater is rare even in its native jungles.

AOUDAD

THE AOUDAD (pronounced "Ah-oo-dad") is often called the Barbary Wild Sheep, for it lives along the Barbary coast of North Africa from the Atlantic Ocean to Tunisia and south through the desert and semi-desert region. "Arui" is the name applied to various sub-species. It is the only wild sheep in Africa.

The most noticeable thing about it, apart from its rather heavy horns about two feet long, is the extremely long hair that clothes its throat and chest and front legs. It stands about three feet high.

The home of the Aoudad is rough, rocky country with much sand and scant vegetation. Waterholes are few and far between, but the animal appears to be able to find enough moisture in the dew that condenses on leaves during the cold nights on the desert. It is, however, greatly dependent on rainfall to maintain grass, weeds and the stunted bush on which it feeds. In periods of continued drought — which may last for years — the Aoudad herds decrease to almost nothing. Hunters, too, take a heavy toll, for the Aoudad is one of the larger animals of the region and an important source of meat for desert tribes. Hide, hair, sinews —all are useful in the economy of the desert.

The sandy color of the animal makes it extremely difficult to see, for it blends perfectly with its desert background.

ONE OF THE most famous of all monkeys is the Barbary Ape, for it is the one that is to be found running at liberty on the great fortress Rock of Gibraltar.

Nobody knows exactly how it got there, for the Rock is on the European side of the Mediterranean, and the true home of this animal is along the shores of the African side of the sea. For that matter, it is curious that the Barbary Ape should even live in Africa, for it belongs to the group of monkeys known as macaques, and the other members of the group are all Asiatic.

Scientists think the Barbary Apes on the Rock of Gibraltar were brought over by traders hundreds of years ago.

The Barbary Ape is about as large as a good-sized dog. It is light yellowish-brown, and it has no tail at all — merely a little fold of skin.

It is said to be a thievish, clever animal, very fond of robbing the vegetable gardens of the Arabs. While a whole troop of the monkeys makes a raid on the gardens, two or three stand guard and when the owners come running out, the guards give the alarm and they all scamper off with the fruits and vegetables they have been able to gather.

ARGALI

THE ARGALI might also be called the Giant Sheep, for it is one of the largest sheep in the world and its body is as bulky as that of a small pony. Its great, wrinkled horns may measure more than a yard along the curve, and skulls of the Argali, with the horns attached, have been found to weigh more than one hundred pounds.

Very few of these magnificent animals have ever been seen outside of their native Siberia and Mongolia, for they live in a bleak and barren land where travel is difficult. The mountain slopes are steep and rocky and the vegetation is scant even in summer. In the winter these great sheep must feed on moss and lichens and dry grass on the more open parts of the mountains where the wind has blown the snow away.

Old writers often said that when an Argali leaps from a great height, it breaks its fall by landing on its heavy horns. This is probably not true, but naturalists *have* seen the animal jump down a ledge thirty feet high and land, unharmed, on its feet.

The famous Marco Polo Sheep lives on the Pamirs of central Asia (a high plateau that is called "the roof of the world") and is one of the Argali group of sheep. The great Venetian explorer, Marco Polo, discovered it more than seven hundred years ago.

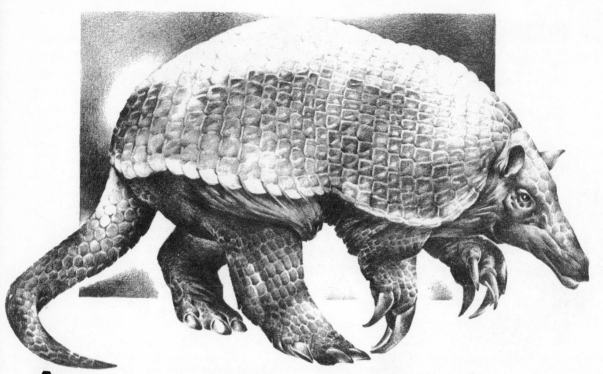

ANIMALS that we call "giants" today are usually only the largest members of their group, and are "giants" only in comparison with others of their own kind. Thus the Giant Armadillo, which is nearly five feet long overall, is surely gigantic in comparison with another little armadillo, the five-inches-long pichiciago. But several million years ago there were *real* Giant Armadillos in South America — creatures seven feet long!

The Giant Armadillo of today lives in the jungles of Dutch Guiana and Brazil. The heavy "armor plating" on its head and body and tail make it look very much like the familiar small nine-banded armadillo of Texas and Louisiana, except, of course, that it is much larger.

These giants are occasionally exhibited in zoological gardens. Surprisingly enough, they are excellent climbers. One summer night in New York's Bronx Zoo a cage door was left open on the side of a building opposite the cage of the Giant Armadillo, and the animal escaped, although it had to climb five fences — three of them seven feet high — in order to get out. The next morning it was easily traced because it had stopped every few yards to dig a hole in its search for ants. The keeper simply followed the trail of holes and found the Giant Armadillo curled up asleep in the last one.

AYE-AYE

ONE OF the strangest and rarest animals in the world is the Aye-Aye of Madagascar — strange because scientists were puzzled for a long time to know whether it belonged to the rodent family or to the lemur family (relatives of the monkeys), and rare because it is found only in Madagascar and even there is scarce.

In size it is hardly larger than a big squirrel; its body is about eighteen inches long, and its bushy tail about the same length. Its fur is dark brown, tipped with white on the top of its head and on its neck. Its ears are very large. But the oddest thing about this night-roaming little creature is its hands and feet—they are extremely long and bony, almost like skeletons of hands and feet. The middle finger on each hand is especially long and is used for pulling grubs out of holes.

Its name is derived from the native term for it — Haihay — and that in turn comes from the sound the Aye-Aye makes. Fortunately for the Aye-Aye, the natives think that anyone who touches it will die within a year, so it is not hunted for food.

Its home is in the dense bamboo forests, where it hunts for insects and is also said to eat the pith of bamboo and sugarcane.

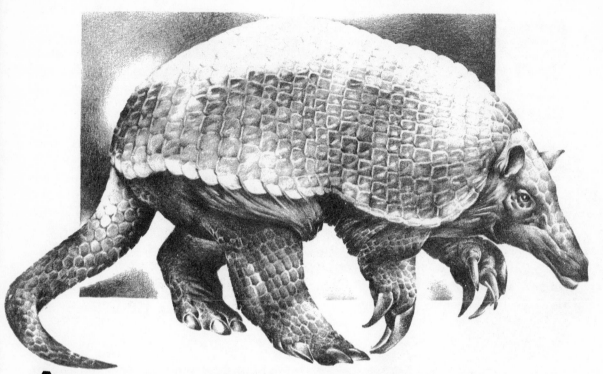

ANIMALS that we call "giants" today are usually only the largest members of their group, and are "giants" only in comparison with others of their own kind. Thus the Giant Armadillo, which is nearly five feet long overall, is surely gigantic in comparison with another little armadillo, the five-inches-long pichiciago. But several million years ago there were *real* Giant Armadillos in South America — creatures seven feet long!

The Giant Armadillo of today lives in the jungles of Dutch Guiana and Brazil. The heavy "armor plating" on its head and body and tail make it look very much like the familiar small nine-banded armadillo of Texas and Louisiana, except, of course, that it is much larger.

These giants are occasionally exhibited in zoological gardens. Surprisingly enough, they are excellent climbers. One summer night in New York's Bronx Zoo a cage door was left open on the side of a building opposite the cage of the Giant Armadillo, and the animal escaped, although it had to climb five fences — three of them seven feet high — in order to get out. The next morning it was easily traced because it had stopped every few yards to dig a hole in its search for ants. The keeper simply followed the trail of holes and found the Giant Armadillo curled up asleep in the last one.

AYE-AYE

ONE OF the strangest and rarest animals in the world is the Aye-Aye of Madagascar — strange because scientists were puzzled for a long time to know whether it belonged to the rodent family or to the lemur family (relatives of the monkeys), and rare because it is found only in Madagascar and even there is scarce.

In size it is hardly larger than a big squirrel; its body is about eighteen inches long, and its bushy tail about the same length. Its fur is dark brown, tipped with white on the top of its head and on its neck. Its ears are very large. But the oddest thing about this night-roaming little creature is its hands and feet—they are extremely long and bony, almost like skeletons of hands and feet. The middle finger on each hand is especially long and is used for pulling grubs out of holes.

Its name is derived from the native term for it — Haihay — and that in turn comes from the sound the Aye-Aye makes. Fortunately for the Aye-Aye, the natives think that anyone who touches it will die within a year, so it is not hunted for food.

Its home is in the dense bamboo forests, where it hunts for insects and is also said to eat the pith of bamboo and sugarcane.

BABOON, HAMADRYAS

THE ancient Egyptians believed that the Hamadryas Baboon was sacred to their god Thoth, and the temples of the city of Hermopolis were devoted to this animal. The bodies of thousands of the "Sacred Baboon" were mummified by the Egyptians.

Today the Hamadryas is not found in Egypt, but in Abyssinia and Arabia. Nevertheless it seems to have been an important animal to the Egyptians thousands of years ago, and many of their sculptures and carvings show it, often sitting with its large mane flowing over its body and with its hands on its knees.

If we can believe the drawings, the Egyptians managed to teach the animal to climb trees and throw dates down to the slaves. That is more than anybody today would try to make a Hamadryas Baboon do, for it has the reputation of being a fierce and untameable animal.

The male Hamadryas has an extraordinarily large, flowing mane of gray hair on its neck and shoulders. Around its tail it has a large patch of bright red, hairless skin.

It is not a large animal — a full-grown Hamadryas Baboon is about the size and weight of a pointer dog — but it looks very large because of its heavy mane of gray hair.

BABIRUSA

IN SOME WAYS, the Babirusa is the most remarkable of all the wild pigs. It is rather large, weighing about two hundred pounds, and it is almost hairless. But the oddest thing about it is the shape of the tusks in old boars.

In the Celebes and Boru, where the Babirusa lives, the natives say that its tusks are like the antlers of a deer, and thus they call it "babirusa," meaning "pig-deer." In most wild swine, the tusks grow from the side of the jaw; in the Babirusa they spring from the top of the muzzle and then curve backward to meet the skull between the eyes, so that they are of little use as weapons. Even the lower tusks are not much good, for they are not kept sharp by rubbing against the upper pair.

Some scientists once thought that maybe the curved upper tusks were useful in protecting the Babirusa's eyes as it rushed through the underbrush, but in that case one would expect the females to have similar "eye fenders." Actually, their upper tusks are much shorter than those of the males.

The Babirusa travels in small herds and likes to be near water. It is a good swimmer. Although it has tiny ears, smaller than those of other pigs, it has a very keen sense of hearing.

LIKE its American cousin, the European Badger has long and grizzled fur, a stout body and short legs. It is, however, considerably larger than the American badger, weighing twenty-five to thirty pounds and being about three feet long, including the seven-inch tail. It has a wide distribution all through Europe and into Asia; other species of Badgers inhabit northern Asia and Japan.

The European Badger has a reputation as a fierce fighter and in ancient days the cruel sport of "badger baiting" with dogs was popular. The animal's loose skin and long hair gives it an advantage; when seized by a dog on almost any part of its body, it can twist and turn inside its loose skin to bite its enemy.

Thick woods or rough tree-clad cliffs are favorite haunts of the Badger, although it also often digs its burrows on fern-clad hillsides. Young Badgers, usually three or four, are born in the deep recesses of the burrows.

The European Badger eats roots, fruits, nuts, birds' eggs and small animals. An old name for it in England is "Brock," and in Germany it is known as the "Dachs" — hence the dachshund, or badger-hound, used in badger-hunting.

BANDICOOT

THERE are several kinds of Bandicoots in Australia and the nearby islands — the Spiny Bandicoot of New Guinea, the Shrew Bandicoot of Dutch New Guinea, the Rabbit Bandicoot or Bilby of Australia itself, and the Pig-footed Bandicoot, also of Australia. Although their names make them sound as if they were entirely unlike, they are actually all recognizably similar.

They have, in general, long and narrow feet with long claws, rather long and tapering snouts, and short tails. They are marsupials — pouched animals — but, oddly, the pouch opens backward instead of forward. All of them are insect or vegetable eaters and nocturnal.

The largest is the Long-legged Bandicoot of New Guinea, with a body about twenty-two inches long and a tail of eight inches. The Shrew Bandicoot is the pigmy of the group, being only nine inches long.

Most of the Bandicoots are gray-brown in color. They used to be extremely common over much of Australia, but they were troublesome around gardens, digging pits in search of mice and insects, and have been exterminated in many areas.

The name "Bandicoot" is a corruption of a native word meaning "pig-rat," which was originally applied to a large rat of India and Ceylon. Nobody knows how it happened to be given to this animal.

LIKE its American cousin, the European Badger has long and grizzled fur, a stout body and short legs. It is, however, considerably larger than the American badger, weighing twenty-five to thirty pounds and being about three feet long, including the seven-inch tail. It has a wide distribution all through Europe and into Asia; other species of Badgers inhabit northern Asia and Japan.

The European Badger has a reputation as a fierce fighter and in ancient days the cruel sport of "badger baiting" with dogs was popular. The animal's loose skin and long hair gives it an advantage; when seized by a dog on almost any part of its body, it can twist and turn inside its loose skin to bite its enemy.

Thick woods or rough tree-clad cliffs are favorite haunts of the Badger, although it also often digs its burrows on fern-clad hillsides. Young Badgers, usually three or four, are born in the deep recesses of the burrows.

The European Badger eats roots, fruits, nuts, birds' eggs and small animals. An old name for it in England is "Brock," and in Germany it is known as the "Dachs" — hence the dachshund, or badger-hound, used in badger-hunting.

BANDICOOT

THERE are several kinds of Bandicoots in Australia and the nearby islands — the Spiny Bandicoot of New Guinea, the Shrew Bandicoot of Dutch New Guinea, the Rabbit Bandicoot or Bilby of Australia itself, and the Pig-footed Bandicoot, also of Australia. Although their names make them sound as if they were entirely unlike, they are actually all recognizably similar.

They have, in general, long and narrow feet with long claws, rather long and tapering snouts, and short tails. They are marsupials — pouched animals — but, oddly, the pouch opens backward instead of forward.

All of them are insect or vegetable eaters and nocturnal.

The largest is the Long-legged Bandicoot of New Guinea, with a body about twenty-two inches long and a tail of eight inches. The Shrew Bandicoot is the pigmy of the group, being only nine inches long.

Most of the Bandicoots are gray-brown in color. They used to be extremely common over much of Australia, but they were troublesome around gardens, digging pits in search of mice and insects, and have been exterminated in many areas.

The name "Bandicoot" is a corruption of a native word meaning "pig-rat," which was originally applied to a large rat of India and Ceylon. Nobody knows how it happened to be given to this animal.

THE Banting is one of a group of wild cattle, which also includes the gayal and the gaur, which may have been the remote ancestors of our present-day domesticated cattle. The Javan Banting is the typical and best-known form; other forms are found on the Malay Peninsula, in Burma, Siam, French Indo-China and Borneo.

The Javan Banting is not as large as some other wild oxen — the gaur, for example — but it stands five feet nine inches at the shoulder, and the record horns are twenty-six and one-half inches on the outside curve. The short hair of adult bulls is blackish-brown or black, and a distinctive characteristic is a large white patch on the rump. Cows are smaller and reddish-chestnut in color.

Being a forest-dwelling animal, the Banting has disappeared in areas where the jungle has been cut down for plantations, and excessive hunting has further depleted its numbers. At present it is quite rare in Java. The flesh is excellent eating and it has been much hunted by the natives for that reason; its hide, too, makes good leather; for horns such as the Banting possesses, the forest people always find plenty of uses as utensils and decorations.

Some Malay peoples keep herds of semi-domesticated Bantings, often crossed with domestic cattle, for the sake of meat and hides.

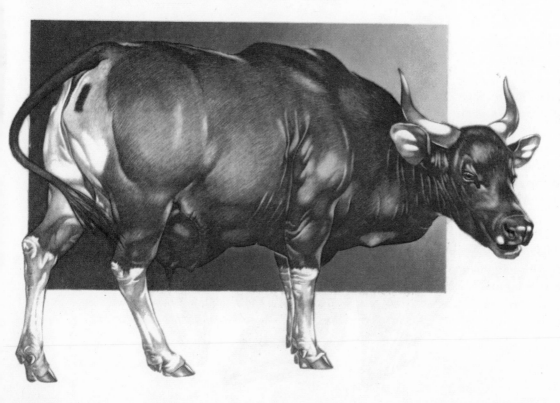

BAT, "FLYING FOX"

THE largest bat in the world is the "Flying Fox" that lives in India, the Malay Peninsula, Australia and other tropical areas of the Pacific. It has a wingspread of more than four feet.

Naturalists call it the "Flying Fox" because its little face is long-nosed and hairy and really looks a good deal like the face of a fox.

There are many kinds of these "Flying Foxes," but they are all large and they all eat fruits. They have definite "roosting places" in certain trees, often in or near native villages, and here they sleep throughout the daylight hours, hanging head-down from the limbs of the tree. Thousands of them may hang in the same tree, and their weight sometimes breaks down the limbs. They sleep in the full sunshine, squirming and twisting as they sleep and occasionally unfolding one enormous wing to fan themselves when the sunshine is too hot.

When dusk comes, they drop off of the tree one by one and take flight, until finally there is a long trail of them across the sky. They may fly many miles to reach an area where jungle trees are in fruit. They usually bite off only a small part of a single fruit and then move on to another one, thus spoiling it. Because they do so much damage to cultivated fruits, they are not allowed to be brought into the United States, even by zoos.

IN ALMOST any part of the United States, when one sees a small bat fluttering through the air at dusk the chances are it is one of the two dozen or more kinds of Little Brown Bats. It is our commonest small bat — it is only about three and a half inches long — and, indeed, some of its kinds are found all around the world.

Like other bats the Little Brown does not fly into anything in the dark because while it flies it sends out a very high-pitched squeak, at about 50,000 cycles a second, and this note "bounces" back from solid objects and warns the bat to turn away. It is a kind of bat radar. Human beings cannot hear this squeak, for we can hear sounds of only some 20,000 cycles a second.

The Little Brown Bat often flies into houses through an open door or window. Most people are afraid of a bat in the house, for they think it is dirty and covered with lice. Bats *do* carry parasites, but they are not the kind that live on human beings. People also think a bat flying around the bedroom is sure to get caught in one's hair. This could happen by accident, but it is not very likely and the best thing to do, if it happens, is to be calm and unhook the bat — and then let it go out of doors. Bats are really useful animals and eat large numbers of flying insects.

The Little Brown Bat lives in caves, hollow trees, under the eaves of houses or in roofs in the daytime. Its chief enemy is the owl, which catches it on the wing at night.

BAT, VAMPIRE

THERE are almost two thousand kinds of bats in the world and most of them are interesting, harmless creatures that feed on insects or fruits; some even sip the nectar of flowers. A few are carnivorous — there are fish-eating bats adept at scooping up small fish from the water. But the Vampire Bat of Mexico and tropical South America is different from all others. It lives entirely on blood.

Its name refers to the legendary vampire or blood-sucking ghost of European literature. Colonists in the New World, finding a bat that drank the blood of people and animals at night, gave the bat its name.

Like most bats, the Vampire sleeps during the day in caves, in trees, under bridges, the eaves of houses, or some other dark place. It emerges at dusk to feed, and in the hot countries finds cattle out of doors and sleeping human beings, often in unscreened houses. It alights on its host, bites quickly and painlessly with its needle-sharp teeth, and then laps the flowing blood. There may be some substance in the bat's saliva that keeps the blood from coagulating rapidly; at any rate, it flows readily and in the morning cattle may often be seen with long ropes of drying blood on their flanks. This blood-letting in itself is seldom harmful, but some individual Bats may be infected with a form of rabies which is usually fatal to the man or animal bitten.

The Vampire has a wing span of only about eight or nine inches.

BEAR, ALASKA BROWN

THE biggest bears in the world live in Alaska and some of them weigh more than 1500 pounds. They are shy and wary and usually run away with a waddling, shuffling gait if they suspect a hunter is near, but if they are cornered or wounded they will attack with lightning speed and terrific ferocity.

All bear cubs are very tiny when they are born, but the cubs of the Alaska Brown Bear are the largest of all. There are two or three of them, born while the mother is hibernating in some snug hole deep under the snow, and they weigh about a pound and a half each.

When a Bear comes out of its winter den in April, it is weak and hungry and at first it feeds like a cow on green grass and alder twigs. Soon various kinds of berries are ripe and it eats these until the salmon begin their spring run in the rivers in June.

The Bear is an expert fisherman. It will wade out into a stream and stand motionless until a salmon swims near. Then, with one swift stroke of the paw, it scoops the fish up and carries it to the bank. Generally it eats only part of the fish and then throws the head and tail and intestines away. In the summertime the Alaska Brown Bear eats huckleberries, skunk cabbage roots, mice, squirrels, and any other small animals it can catch.

BEAR, BLACK

THE SMALLEST bear in North America is the Black Bear, and it is also the commonest, since it is found in thickly wooded areas all over the continent. A full-grown Black Bear averages between two and three hundred pounds, but may weigh up to nearly five hundred pounds.

This is the Bear that is sometimes seen tied up with a chain at filling stations and roadside restaurants in many parts of the country. A Black Bear in the woods is usually not dangerous unless it is wounded or defending its cubs, but "tame" Bears along the roadside are tricky and have sometimes killed their keepers.

All through the summer the Black Bear feeds on berries, fruits, honey, ants, fish, mice, ground squirrels and so on. Well larded with fat, when cold weather comes it "dens up" in a cave or a hollow tree or under a log, and sleeps through the winter. The cubs (usually two) are born while the mother is denned up. They are tiny creatures weighing only nine to twelve ounces. When spring comes, the mother leads them out of the den and begins their education—teaching them how to catch mice, how to turn over stones to find grubs, how to dig for roots and how to climb trees when danger threatens. A Black Bear can run very fast and can climb a tree almost as quickly as a squirrel.

BEAR, EUROPEAN BROWN

WILD WOODED places all across Europe and northern Asia are the homes of the various kinds of Brown Bears — huge animals that are sometimes more than eight feet long from the tip of the snout to the beginning of the tiny, two-inch tail.

The European Brown Bear is not a sociable animal and it is rare to see two of them together in the forests, unless they are a mother and her cubs. There are usually two of the babies and they are born as small, hairless creatures while the mother is hidden away for her winter's sleep. But they grow rapidly and are well covered with fur when the mother leads them forth in the spring.

Although a Brown Bear may be quite fat when it begins its winter sleep, much of this fat disappears during the winter.

Many stories are told of the fearsome "bear hug," in which a bear is supposed to grasp a man and squeeze him to death. Naturalists do not believe a bear actually kills a man by hugging him in this manner, but a bear can be very dangerous with its large, heavily-clawed paws.

In the Middle Ages, and even in recent years in some parts of Europe, travelling bands of gypsies exhibited Brown Bears which have been taught to "dance." This is not a real dance, but a kind of shuffle which the bears easily learn to do.

BEAVER

BEAR, EUROPEAN

THE BEAVER played a truly important part in the early settlement of the United States and Canada. At one time it was very plentiful all over North America as far south as the Rio Grande, and its fur was so valuable that it sold by the ounce.

Today the Beaver has been killed off in many parts of the United States but in a few states successful efforts are being made to increase its numbers in waste land.

It is nature's greatest engineer. Colonies of Beavers, often a dozen or more family groups, settle in swampy areas and gnaw down small trees whose limbs they pile up in mounds that may be six feet high and twelve feet across. These are plastered with mud, and inside are the grass-lined winter-

ing quarters. Then, downstream, the Beavers construct a dam of logs and branches and mud which causes the water to back up around the lodge. So expert are the Beavers that their dams never raise the water high enough to flood the sleeping quarters inside the lodge.

The Beaver has tremendously-developed gnawing teeth that enable it to "bite down" even trees that are eighteen inches in diameter, although it usually fells much smaller trees. These it stores up under water so it can eat the bark during the winter. It uses its flat, broad tail to steer with while swimming, and does not use it to pat down the mud.

CONSIDERABLE numbers of the small antelopes known as Blesboks still roam the south African veldt, but in game preserves and on the huge farms, for the Blesbok has long since been exterminated as a free wild species over much of its former range.

Nevertheless the habits of the animal have not greatly changed, and the Blesbok is still a shy and wary creature. Explorers have told of its habit of wandering over the plains, always heading into the wind and with its nose to the ground. When an enemy — perhaps a hunter — comes into the ante-lope's range, the herds take off at high speed, and their alarm sets off other herds in the far distance, which also start running.

The Blesbok stands about three feet two inches high at the shoulder. One must be quite familiar with antelopes to distinguish it from another small African antelope, the bontebok; the most easily recognized difference between them is that the white "blaze" on the face of the bontebok runs right up to the root of the horns, and in the Blesbok it is crossed by a narrow dark line just below the eyes.

The Blesbok has dark, purple-red hair, and a graceful set of lyre-shaped horns. It is a grazing animal.

BOAR, EUROPEAN WILD

FOR HUNDREDS and perhaps even thousands of years men have hunted the Wild Boar in Europe and Asia, and while it is hard to think of a pig as a "game" animal, the Wild Boar is so fierce and so courageous that all the skill and daring of the huntsman are needed in its pursuit. In olden times it was the custom to make a boar hunt just before Christmas and to serve a boar's head at the Christmas feast.

The Wild Boar has been exterminated in England for more than three hundred years, but it still roams the thick forests of the continent of Europe and is still hunted with packs of dogs. Even hunting the Boar with high-powered modern rifles is dangerous sport, for it attacks fearlessly and swiftly. A big Boar may weigh as much as three hundred pounds and its tusks are like sharp, six-inch daggers.

It is easy to tell where a Wild Boar has passed through a forest, for the earth is rooted up and dead wood is turned over by the animal's snout as it searches for roots, bulbs, fungus or even small animals.

The Boar's upper tusks keep growing all through life and are worn down and kept sharp by rubbing against the lower tusks. If one of these is broken off, the upper tusk sometimes grows in a long curve that drives it into the animal's skull, finally killing it.

A LITTLE smaller than its relative, the European wild boar, the Indian species weighs between two hundred and three hundred pounds. It has three-inch tusks which are kept razor-sharp by rubbing against each other. The animal averages thirty to forty inches in shoulder height.

"Pig-sticking" — the hunting of the Indian Wild Boar from horseback, with lances as weapons — is a dangerous sport, for the animal is reckless and fearless. It is even recorded that Wild Boars will on occasion charge an elephant, and they can give even a hungry tiger a hard fight.

Damp forests, bushlands, tall grass and swampy reed patches are the lairs of the Wild Boar, for here it finds the roots that it eats. Occasionally it raids native gardens, rooting up and destroying the crops during the night. Like all pigs, wild or domestic, it will eat almost anything, even carrion. Some Wild Boars are said to have learned to dig up fish of certain species which bury themselves in the mud during the dry season.

Old Boars are usually solitary and travel by themselves; females and young associate together in small herds.

BONGO

THE BONGO has often been called the handsomest of all the antelopes. Its short, glossy hair is a rich brownish-red that harmonizes well with the creamy stripes that cross its back and sides. Its horns have an upward lift at the end that emphasizes the height of the animal, and its eyes are especially noticeable, being large and bright.

While perhaps not the rarest antelope in Africa, it is one that is seldom seen alive because of its shyness. It inhabits the dense tropical forests, where the undergrowth on which it feeds is in almost perpetual gloom. Apparently it has adjusted its sight and ways of life to the semi-darkness of the forest, for specimens in captivity appear to dis-

like bright days and voluntarily go out of doors only on gloomy, overcast days.

An adult male stands about three feet seven inches at the shoulder, with horns that average about twenty inches in length; the record is a little more than thirty-six inches. Both males and females carry horns. They are sharply pointed and are useful weapons; leopards may occasionally kill young Bongos, but would scarcely dare attack an adult. Nevertheless, they are often taken in pits and snares by African tribesmen, and strips of Bongo hide are a favorite ornament of native dancers and sorcerers.

BROCKET

CENTRAL and South America have several species of small deer that are known as Brockets. Some of them are only about nineteen inches high, although they range up to "big" Brockets that are around two and a half feet high.

We are likely to think of deer as having large and many-branched antlers, but the Brockets have short, simple, spike-like antlers about three inches long. Most of these animals are reddish-brown. Oddly enough, one of their distinguishing marks is a pair of "cowlicks" in which their hair radiates in all directions. One of these is on the top of the head and the other on the face, just below the eyes.

The Brockets live in rather open country and hunters say they never travel in herds — they either go alone, or a male and a female travel together. They seem to stay together as long as they live. The young Brockets are born in what is mid-summer in South America — in December or January — and in three to five days they are strong enough and fleet enough to follow their mother.

All of the Brockets are swift, at least for a short distance, but in open country a horse can run them down after a little while.

BUFFALO, CAPE

SOME HUNTERS of big game claim that the Cape Buffalo is the most dangerous hoofed animal in the world. Stocky and heavily-built, an old bull stands nearly five feet high at the shoulder and has massive, broad horns that may be as much as three and a half feet wide from bend to bend.

However, it is not the size of the animal nor its horns that make it dangerous; it is the ferocity and tenacity of its attack when wounded or when cows are guarding their young. Heavy bullets are said scarcely to slow the charge of a Buffalo unless they strike just above the eyes in the narrow line of division between the horns.

The African Buffaloes and the Indian, or Water, Buffaloes, are the only animals that can properly be called Buffaloes, although that name is widely used for the American bison. There are various kinds of African Buffaloes, but the Cape Buffalo is probably the best known. It has been exterminated over much of its former range in southern Africa but survives in some numbers in eastern Africa.

It likes country where there is plenty of water and grazing. Unfortunately these same localities are often preferable for plantations, and the Buffalo has been killed off; it is also highly susceptible to the cattle disease known as rinderpest.

BURRHEL

IN THE HIGH, cold, rocky mountains of Tibet lives a curious wild sheep that in some ways is so like the wild goats that zoologists have often been puzzled how to classify it. This is the Burrhel (sometimes spelled Bharal), or Blue Sheep. It is generally agreed that, since it does not have a beard and a strong odor like the goats, it should be more properly considered a wild sheep.

Its name of Blue Sheep comes from the fact that its smooth, close hair is a peculiar tone of gray that in certain lights looks almost blue.

The Burrhel is about three feet high and has immense, curving horns. It is certainly goat-like in its ability to climb, for it lives at great heights in the mountains — at 10,000 to 16,000 feet — where the steep slopes are barren and rocky. It can leap from rock to rock with all the agility of the surest-footed goat.

Naturally, in such a bleak and desolate country, few people pass through the Burrhel territory except hunters and travellers, and the animal is comparatively safe, for it can climb and run with ease on cliffs where no man dare move except a few inches at a time. Food is scarce and confined to grasses and small bushes, and these the Burrhel crops closely during the daytime, frequently lying down to rest among the stones and so blending into their color that it is difficult to see.

CACOMISTLE

ALTHOUGH the Cacomistle is fairly common in the southwestern part of the United States and Mexico, this small, slender, ring-tailed relative of the raccoons is seldom seen because it lives mostly in woods, and comes out of hiding only at night.

It is called by a variety of names — Cacomixl, Ringtail, Ring-tailed Cat, Civet-cat, Coon-cat and Bassarisk, for example. Its fur is grayish-brown and its tail is ringed with white bands. Its over-all length is about thirty-two inches, and its tail is seventeen inches long.

The Cacomistle is a strong and fierce hunter of rats, mice, other small animals, as well as birds and insects. It is such a good "ratter" that people in the Cacomistle country sometimes keep one as a pet just for the purpose of hunting rats. Unfortunately when it can it likes to make a meal of poultry.

It makes its home in holes in the trees or rocks, and in these nests the young are born in May or June. There are usually three or four.

In Mexico the natives claim to have a way of knowing whether a hole in a tree is actually occupied by a family of Cacomistles. They say that if the bark has been removed from around the hole, it is a sure sign that the animals are living there.

IN THE HIGH, cold, rocky mountains of Tibet lives a curious wild sheep that in some ways is so like the wild goats that zoologists have often been puzzled how to classify it. This is the Burrhel (sometimes spelled Bharal), or Blue Sheep. It is generally agreed that, since it does not have a beard and a strong odor like the goats, it should be more properly considered a wild sheep.

Its name of Blue Sheep comes from the fact that its smooth, close hair is a peculiar tone of gray that in certain lights looks almost blue.

The Burrhel is about three feet high and has immense, curving horns. It is certainly goat-like in its ability to climb, for it lives at great heights in the mountains — at 10,000 to 16,000 feet — where the steep slopes are barren and rocky. It can leap from rock to rock with all the agility of the surest-footed goat.

Naturally, in such a bleak and desolate country, few people pass through the Burrhel territory except hunters and travellers, and the animal is comparatively safe, for it can climb and run with ease on cliffs where no man dare move except a few inches at a time. Food is scarce and confined to grasses and small bushes, and these the Burrhel crops closely during the daytime, frequently lying down to rest among the stones and so blending into their color that it is difficult to see.

CACOMISTLE

ALTHOUGH the Cacomistle is fairly common in the southwestern part of the United States and Mexico, this small, slender, ring-tailed relative of the raccoons is seldom seen because it lives mostly in woods, and comes out of hiding only at night.

It is called by a variety of names — Cacomixl, Ringtail, Ring-tailed Cat, Civet-cat, Coon-cat and Bassarisk, for example. Its fur is grayish-brown and its tail is ringed with white bands. Its over-all length is about thirty-two inches, and its tail is seventeen inches long.

The Cacomistle is a strong and fierce hunter of rats, mice, other small animals, as well as birds and insects. It is such a good "ratter" that people in the Cacomistle country sometimes keep one as a pet just for the purpose of hunting rats. Unfortunately when it can it likes to make a meal of poultry.

It makes its home in holes in the trees or rocks, and in these nests the young are born in May or June. There are usually three or four.

In Mexico the natives claim to have a way of knowing whether a hole in a tree is actually occupied by a family of Cacomistles. They say that if the bark has been removed from around the hole, it is a sure sign that the animals are living there.

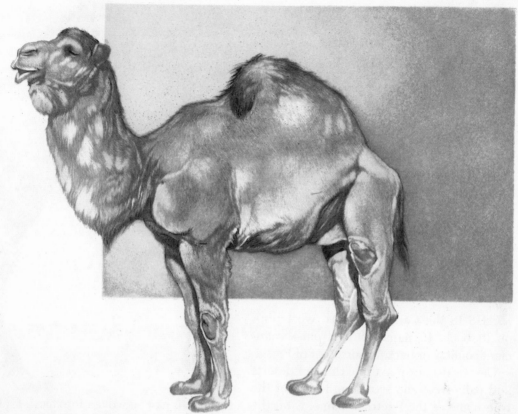

ON THE HOT, sandy wastes of Arabia and the neighboring countries the one-humped Arabian Camel, or Dromedary, is a familiar sight, for it is marvellously adapted to life on the deserts where it must often go for days without food or water.

The "ship of the desert," as it is fancifully called, has great, pad-like feet that sink but very little into the yielding sand. During a sandstorm it can close its nostrils to keep out the flying dust, and its eyes are well protected by a double row of eyelashes.

It is often believed that a Camel can go nine days without water, but actually not many of them can go longer than three days, especially if they are carrying heavy loads. Nevertheless, there are records that seem to be true of some Camels going as long as thirty-four days without water. When it can get all the water it wants, it drinks five to seven gallons a day.

A good riding Dromedary can travel nearly one hundred miles in a day, and once a camel travelled one hundred and fifteen miles in eleven hours in Egypt.

CAMEL, BACTRIAN

THIS IS the Camel that has two humps on its back. Its name comes from the ancient country of Bactria, northeast of Persia.

Camels usually make one think of deserts and palm trees and scorching heat, but the true home of the Bactrian Camel is on the bleak and arid plains of central Asia where the winters are bitterly cold and snowy. Here the Camel grows a coat of thick hair for protection. It is a domesticated animal — there are no wild Camels — and is dependent upon man for any food it gets other than the dried grasses and leaves of stunted bushes.

Life would be almost impossible for the people of this desolate region without the Camel, for it provides them with transportation, food and shelter. Camel milk and Camel meat are highly prized, and the soft,

warm hair can be woven into cloth for tents and clothing.

The larger breeds of Camels are used to carry baggage. An average load is about four hundred pounds, but for short distances it can carry several times that weight. A baggage Camel seldom goes more than three miles an hour. A big baggage Camel will measure about seven feet to the top of its humps. These humps are a storehouse of fatty material, and when a Camel is overworked or food is scarce it "lives on its hump." Thus, if the humps are flabby, it is a sign the Camel is not in good condition.

THE CHAMOIS, one of the goat-like antelopes, is supposed to be one of the surest-footed of all animals and certainly there are not many that are its equal at jumping from one jagged pinnacle of rock to another without slipping and tumbling down to death. Hunters have told of seeing Chamois in the Alps standing on a point of rock only about the size of a half-dollar piece, with all four feet bunched on that tiny point.

The Chamois lives in the mountains of Europe — in the Pyrenees between France and Spain, in the Alps of Switzerland and in the rugged Carpathians and Caucasus. Actually it is not so much of a mountain-dwelling creature as we are likely to think, and is more often found in the forested slopes of the mountains than among the barren rocks. Its winter color is chestnut-brown, but in spring it takes on a lighter, grayer hue. The males, or bucks, weigh from fifty to seventy pounds.

The herds of Chamois are made up of fifteen or twenty animals. At daybreak they start feeding but in the middle of the day they seek the shelter of rocks or trees and lie in the shade until dusk. Lichens and the various kinds of low-growing plants that live high up on the mountains are their food.

CHEVROTAIN

ANOTHER common name for the Chevrotain, the "Mouse-deer," gives one a good idea of the size and appearance of this delicate and dainty little creature. The only misleading thing about the name is that it is neither a mouse nor a deer. Actually it is placed by the naturalists in a little group all its own.

There are two kinds of Chevrotains, one found in the forests of the Congo and West Africa and the other in southern Asia, but they are much alike. The Indian species is prettily spotted with white on a body color of brown minutely speckled with yellow. It stands about ten to twelve inches high and weighs only five or six pounds.

These slender-legged little creatures are timid and shy and creep through the tall grass with all the quietness of a mouse. They seldom venture out of shelter to feed on leaves and grasses except in the mornings and evenings. Their habit of walking stiff-legged has given rise to the erroneous belief that they have no joints or "knees" in their legs. They are fairly plentiful in forest areas, and many are snared by native hunters for food.

The Chevrotains need to be shy and wary, for they have no horns for defense and the jungles where they live abound with enemies of every kind, from the various wild cats to big monitor lizards and even snakes.

THE SWIFTEST animal in the world for short distances is the Cheetah, or Hunting Leopard, of Africa and India. Cheetahs have been "clocked" at seventy miles an hour, but they slow up considerably after a run of a quarter of a mile. A Cheetah has long, slender legs and a powerfully-muscled body; its legs are actually longer than those of any other member of the cat family, for it stands almost two and three-quarters feet high.

For untold centuries the great princes of India have kept tame Hunting Leopards to run down the small but exceeding swift and agile blackbuck. When the game is sighted, a hood is placed over the animal's eyes. At the right moment the hood is removed. A quick glance around and it sights the game. Then it begins a quiet stalk toward the antelope through the low bush. When it is about two hundred yards away, it leaps forward and makes a straight run toward the blackbuck, which takes off at top speed with a series of bounding leaps. Almost invariably a good Cheetah will bring down the game after a short run.

The Cheetah is the only cat animal whose claws cannot be retarded or drawn into their sheaths among the pads of the feet.

CHIMPANZEE

THE CHIMPANZEE is one of the anthropoid, or man-like, apes. It lives in the vast tropical rain-forest that stretches across the center of Africa.

It is probably the best-known of all the great apes, for it is extensively used as an experimental animal in the study of human diseases, and because it is relatively common and easily obtained. Lists of the "ten most intelligent animals" invariably mention the Chimpanzee because of its imitative ability which enables it to perform many "human" feats, such as riding a bicycle. Behavior studies have shown that it has a good reasoning power;

test animals, for instance, learn to pile up boxes to reach food above their heads.

An adult male Chimpanzee stands about five feet high, weighs one hundred and twenty-five to one hundred and seventy-five pounds. Females are perhaps a foot shorter and weigh one hundred to one hundred and fifty pounds. In both sexes the hair is long and black.

Chimpanzees travel in small groups or family parties, feeding on wild fruits. Although they can stand and walk upright, they generally travel on all fours, with the hands doubled up.

IN ASIA and Africa live several kinds of rather small, long-tailed, spotted or striped, cat-like animals called Civets, or Civet-cats. They are quite short-legged and long-bodied and their general body color is grayish-brown.

The Civet possesses glands which secrete a very strong, sweetish scent and many years ago it was hunted for the sake of this scent, which was used in the making of perfume. Actually it is not a very pleasant smell — as anyone can testify who has entered a Small Mammal House in a zoo on a warm summer day and has stopped in front of a Civet cage — but it has a peculiar, lasting quality that makes it very valuable in perfumery. Naturally, the scent is changed and disguised in the perfume; it is used only as a base or foundation for other scents.

In general the Civet is a shy and solitary animal, hiding in the forests, bushes or thick grass during the day and coming out into more open country only at night. The natives are not very fond of it because of its habit of killing poultry, but in the wild it feeds on birds and small animals, snakes, frogs, insects, eggs and even fruits.

Wherever the Civet goes, it leaves a trail of its scent behind and there are many stories of hunting dogs chasing other game but branching off and starting to chase the Civet when they run across its track.

COATI-MUNDI

ONE OF the most mischievous members of the raccoon family is the Coati-Mundi of Mexico south through Central America to Paraguay. Generally reddish-brown in color, with a long, brown- or black-ringed tail and an extraordinarily long and slender nose, it is a grotesque little creature about the size of a full-grown cat. Cats are supposed to have a great deal of curiosity, but a Coati-Mundi is *all* curiosity; it wants to know everything about everything.

In Central and South America this little animal is often kept as a pet, but if it is not chained up or locked in a cage, it is liable to explore one's house so thoroughly that the next morning everything will be scratched or broken open or knocked off the shelf.

The Coati usually travels through the jungles in small troops of half a dozen to a score of individuals, always in search of food. It eats fruits, young birds, eggs, lizards and insects, and is said to have a clever way of catching the big lizards known as iguanas. When Coatis are scampering through the trees and come upon an iguana basking on a limb, the lizard often drops to the ground and runs to another tree, with the Coatis in full chase. However, the Coatis seem to have learned this lizard habit, and sometimes they split up their troop so that some stay on the ground, while the others hunt through the trees. Then, when the iguana drops to the ground, the Coatis under the tree are sure to catch it.

IN ASIA and Africa live several kinds of rather small, long-tailed, spotted or striped, cat-like animals called Civets, or Civet-cats. They are quite short-legged and long-bodied and their general body color is grayish-brown.

The Civet possesses glands which secrete a very strong, sweetish scent and many years ago it was hunted for the sake of this scent, which was used in the making of perfume. Actually it is not a very pleasant smell — as anyone can testify who has entered a Small Mammal House in a zoo on a warm summer day and has stopped in front of a Civet cage — but it has a peculiar, lasting quality that makes it very valuable in perfumery. Naturally, the scent is changed and disguised in the perfume; it is used only as a base or foundation for other scents.

In general the Civet is a shy and solitary animal, hiding in the forests, bushes or thick grass during the day and coming out into more open country only at night. The natives are not very fond of it because of its habit of killing poultry, but in the wild it feeds on birds and small animals, snakes, frogs, insects, eggs and even fruits.

Wherever the Civet goes, it leaves a trail of its scent behind and there are many stories of hunting dogs chasing other game but branching off and starting to chase the Civet when they run across its track.

COATI-MUNDI

ONE OF the most mischievous members of the raccoon family is the Coati-Mundi of Mexico south through Central America to Paraguay. Generally reddish-brown in color, with a long, brown- or black-ringed tail and an extraordinarily long and slender nose, it is a grotesque little creature about the size of a full-grown cat. Cats are supposed to have a great deal of curiosity, but a Coati-Mundi is *all* curiosity; it wants to know everything about everything.

In Central and South America this little animal is often kept as a pet, but if it is not chained up or locked in a cage, it is liable to explore one's house so thoroughly that the next morning everything will be scratched or broken open or knocked off the shelf.

The Coati usually travels through the jungles in small troops of half a dozen to a score of individuals, always in search of food. It eats fruits, young birds, eggs, lizards and insects, and is said to have a clever way of catching the big lizards known as iguanas. When Coatis are scampering through the trees and come upon an iguana basking on a limb, the lizard often drops to the ground and runs to another tree, with the Coatis in full chase. However, the Coatis seem to have learned this lizard habit, and sometimes they split up their troop so that some stay on the ground, while the others hunt through the trees. Then, when the iguana drops to the ground, the Coatis under the tree are sure to catch it.

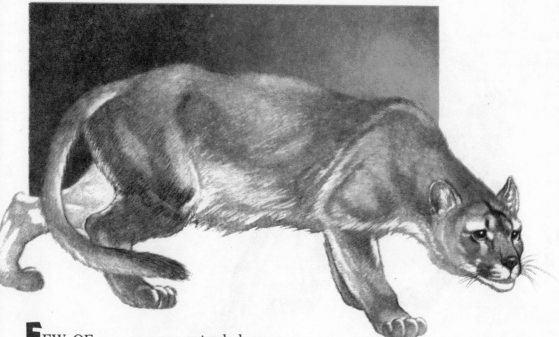

FEW OF our common animals have so many names as the Cougar, for it is often called the Puma, Mountain Lion, Panther, Painter, Catamount and so on. Not many of our animals have such a bad reputation, either, for the Cougar has been the "villain" in many a stirring story of pioneer life.

It is a big cat, eight feet long over-all, and may weigh more than two hundred pounds. Its fur is brownish and rather dull-colored.

Hunters say that the Cougar is one of the most difficult of all animals to see; it is so expert in hiding that although woodsmen may see its tracks everywhere and be sure it is plentiful, they seldom catch a glimpse of the animal itself.

It used to be found over much of the United States as far north as the Great Lakes and up into Maine and lower Canada, but now it has disappeared from all except the wilder parts. It likes wild, broken country where there is plenty of food, such as deer and wapiti.

When the Cougar kills a large animal and has eaten all it wants, it often covers the carcass with brush and returns later for a second or a third meal.

The scream, or yell, of a Cougar is a fearsome thing and many woodsmen have told how startled and frightened they were by its long, drawn-out cry. Usually the animal hides or slinks away, and makes no attempt to attack a man, but there are rare instances of its killing children.

COYOTE

THE RANCHER riding the range in the western United States may sometimes see a small, sandy-grayish creature resembling a shepherd dog as it trots along through the sagebrush. At any slight rise in the land it is likely to seek the highest part and turn to watch him intently. That is the Coyote, or Prairie Wolf, that is such a characteristic animal of the western North America.

But the Coyote is a shy and wily wolf and although it has not been driven out of the great regions now under cultivation or used for cattle ranching, it keeps out of sight as much as possible. Even where it is seldom seen, it is often heard — for the Coyote gives voice to its wild, half-chattering, half-wailing cry at sunrise and again at sunset. It is

one of the lonesomest, most mournful sounds in the world and yet one that Westerners like to hear, for it reminds them of nights and days on the prairie, of long rides under the open sky and of the pungent smell of the sagebrush fires.

Stockmen consider the Coyote a pest, for it kills sheep and poultry. Thousands of Coyotes are hunted down every year. Nevertheless, it is of considerable value in killing small rodents, which are perhaps the largest part of its diet, along with birds, lizards, insects and carrion.

The Coyote is a fast runner — faster than all but the swiftest breeds of dogs — and takes refuge in flight when it is frightened.

ANYONE seeing a Coypu for the first time might think it was an especially large muskrat. Its body, about two feet long, is clothed in dark yellowish-brown or reddish-brown hair and its tail is long and ratlike. Like the muskrat, it is an animal of lakes, streams, and swamps — but in South America, rather than in North America.

Another name for the Coypu is Nutria, and the fur of the animal is usually sold in the fur markets under the name of Nutria. Many years ago the soft underfur was in great demand as a base for fine hats for men and even today it is used somewhat for that purpose, though its chief use is in the making of fur coats. The Coypu has been hunted so greatly for the sake of its fur that it is almost extinct in many places, and Argentina has placed the sale of skins under government control. Now many of the animals are reared on game farms.

In the wild it lives in burrows along the edge of the water or in platform-like nests among the reeds at the water's edge. Here, where the water is still and quiet, it often gathers in little groups to swim and play. Baby Coypus are good swimmers, but naturalists have seen them trying to ride on their mother's back while she is in the water.

The Coypu feeds on roots and water plants and sometimes on shellfish.

CUSCUS

SEVERAL kinds of Cuscuses live in Australia, New Guinea and on the islands in the region roundabout. All of them are slow and easy-going creatures—the largest about the size of a large cat. They live in trees and have long, grasping tails. Like cats, their eyes have vertical pupils.

One of the largest and most interesting is the Spotted Cuscus of New Guinea, Queensland, New Britain and the Admiralty Islands. It is one of the few mammals of the world in which the color pattern of the male is very much different from that of the female. Although the colors of the Spotted Cuscus vary somewhat in different places, the difference in the Cuscuses found in Queensland, Australia, are typical. The male is white with gray spots and the female is simply gray above and white beneath. The animal is about three and a half feet long, and almost half of its length is tail.

The Cuscus has very thick fur and its little ears are almost buried in the fur. Oddly enough, the fur only extends part of the way down the tail, and the end is bare, like the tail of an oppossum. It is this bare part that the animal uses to hold on with when it is climbing through the trees. It feeds on fruits, small animals, birds' eggs and big snails, hunting food at night and sleeping among the thick foliage or in hollow trees by day.

The Cuscus is a marsupial — that is, it cradles its newborn babies in a pouch. It has one or two babies at a time.

THE DEER with this unlovely name is a native of India and Burma and is quite a small creature, being only about two feet high at the shoulders. However, it did not get its name from the fact that it is small or hog-like, but rather because of its way of running. When frightened, it is likely to put its head down and gallop forward in the way a hog runs, instead of bounding and leaping as many other deer do. Its favorite haunts are grassy plains, among grass tall enough to shelter it but not tall enough to hide buffalo and rhinoceroses.

Leopards and big pythons are the Hog Deer's worst enemies, although it can defend itself quite well with its twelve-inch, sharp-pointed antlers.

The general tone of the deer's hair is brownish with a yellowish or reddish tinge, but each hair is tipped with white and thus it has rather a speckled appearance. The fawns are white-spotted at birth and remain dappled until they are about six months old. Presumably this common coloring of new-born deer is nature's camouflage, and helps to protect them from enemies.

Hog Deer usually travel singly or in little groups of two or three animals.

DEER, MULE

THE PLAINS and "bad lands" of the western United States are the home of the Mule Deer — so called because of its extremely large ears similar to those of a mule. Another name for it is the Black-tailed Deer.

It prefers to live in wild and broken country, among the mountains and foothills, where great rocks and ravines and scattered brush give the landscape a forbidding air. Rather short-legged and stocky of body, the Mule Deer has all the strength and speed it needs to escape such enemies as wolves and cougars. It runs with tremendous jumps, leaping into the air with all four feet and landing on all fours. Of course, this method of running is not as fast as the gait of some deer, but it is a great advantage in such rough country.

In the wintertime, the Mule Deer gather in rather large groups and feed mostly in the sheltered lowlands. With the coming of spring and the melting of the snow, they break up into small parties of two or three or wander off by themselves, and move up into the mountains to feed on grass, twigs, the leaves of low trees and shrubs, acorns and the like.

Mule Deer bucks weigh about one hundred and fifty to two hundred pounds, on an average, and stand three and a half feet high at the shoulder. The females, or does, are a little smaller.

DEER, EUROPEAN RED

THIS IS THE common deer of much of Europe and is found also, in some of its forms, over a large part of Asia. Nowadays, of course, the Red Deer does not roam wild over the continents as it did hundreds of years ago, but great herds are still preserved on the large estates in England.

It is a large deer, standing fully four feet at the shoulder, and its antlers are peculiar in having a large number of tines, or points. One set of antlers was found to have sixty-six points — but this, of course, was considerably more than the normal number.

The Red Deer actually is red in color — at least, in summer, it is a bright reddish-brown. The fur becomes longer in winter and is more of a brownish-gray color.

Young male animals are called harts, and the females are known as hinds.

Fully grown male Red Deer are known as stags and these are the lords of the herd until they are vanquished in autumn fights by some younger and sturdier male. Stags generally drop their antlers in February or March, but young animals keep theirs until later in the spring. New ones start to grow immediately.

DINGO

THE DINGO, or Warrigal, is a wild dog of Australia, but how it got to Australia is a mystery that may never be solved. Scientists believe that in prehistoric times it was brought to the island-continent by primitive men. At any rate, it is well established in Australia now.

In the wild, the Dingo does not bark, although it *can* make yelping and howling sounds, and often learns to imitate domestic dogs.

Its appearance is very much like that of any yellow-haired mongrel and it is about the size of a small collie, with rather short yellowish-brown hair. Dingo puppies are quite as cute and appealing as the puppies of domestic dogs. Nevertheless, they are wild animals and may be dangerous when they grow up.

The Dingo is not common now because it has been severely hunted. It has a very bad habit of killing sheep, often destroying far more than it eats, and it is destructive to poultry too.

The Australian bushmen sometimes use Dingoes as hunting dogs, but they are not very good for they are apt to run away. The natives say when a Dingo gets tired of hunting it stops and refuses to go any further—so the owner has to pick it up and carry it home on his shoulder!

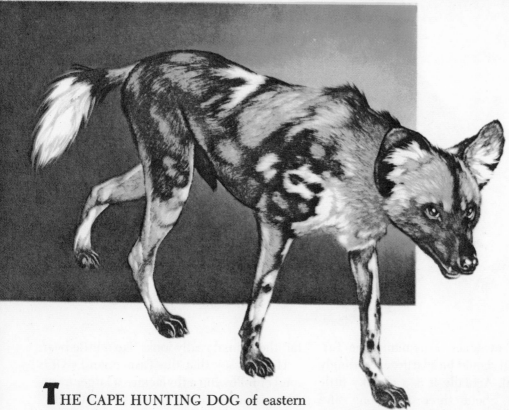

THE CAPE HUNTING DOG of eastern and southern Africa looks almost as much like a hyaena as a dog, and it is as fierce as it looks. Pups have been tamed, but they do not stay docile.

This big, powerful dog with a short and broad muzzle is heavily spotted with yellow, brown, black, gray and white irregular patches, and its short hair is coarse and oily.

It is always found in packs of four to sixty, usually about fifteen, and when the pack takes up the chase it is an exceptionally fleet and hardy animal that can escape. The dogs hunt tirelessly and with extraordinary skill and cunning; some of them may cut off across country to intercept a circling animal and station themselves along its probable line of flight.

A pack of Hunting Dogs was once seen to dash into a herd of cattle a hundred yards from a ranch house and drive the cows over a nearby hill. By the time the farmer could throw a saddle on his horse and reach the spot, the Hunting Dogs had killed a cow and eaten the carcass down to the bones. Large numbers of sheep and cattle are killed by the dogs.

The Cape Hunting Dog lives mostly in open plains regions. Its pups, as many as twelve in a litter, are born in nests underground.

DEVIL, TASMANIAN

ON THE evidence of its name, the Tasmanian Devil should be a large, exceedingly fierce animal. Actually it is a chunky little fellow only about three feet long and though it is savage enough in the wild, it is dangerous only to poultry raisers, small wallabies, ground birds and lizards in its native Tasmania. In fact, young Tasmanian Devils, when hand-reared and treated with kindness, are said to make excellent and amusing pets.

At one time the Tasmanian Devil was found both on the continent of Australia and on the island of Tasmania, but now it is only to be seen on the island. The whole body and the upper part of the tail are covered with long, coarse, black hair and there are irregular blotches of white on the shoulders, throat and rump. Except for its tail the animal really looks like a little bear.

Hunters say that the Tasmanian Devil is fond of following a thylacine—a larger meat-eating animal—on its rounds. When the thylacine kills a wallaby or some other small kangaroo, it is likely to eat a small portion and then go away. The Tasmanian Devil comes along and eats what is left.

The Tasmanian Devil (like other Australian animals) is a marsupial and carries its babies (one to four) in a backward-facing pouch. The babies can climb a tree easily, although they lose this ability somewhat as they grow older.

When a Tasmanian Devil is angry or frightened, it makes a weird variety of sounds — a whining growl, a snarling cough, and a low, yelling growl.

THIS SAVAGE-LOOKING baboon is a cousin of the equally hideous Mandrill, both of which live in West Africa. One explanation of the name "Drill" is that it is a very old English word meaning baboon or ape. A Mandrill is, by that account, a "man-ape."

The Drill is a heavily-muscled, powerful animal. Walking on all fours like a dog, it has a deliberate and confident air as if it knows just exactly how strong and dangerous it is. Drills have often been exhibited in the Bronx Zoo and all of them have had the habit of yawning frequently, to show their long teeth. They yawn so often, when they can not possibly be sleepy, that it is supposed this is a gesture that may serve to frighten other animals.

The bare skin around the Drill's tail is bright red and most of its body is dark blue, although the skin is usually well hidden by the thick grayish-brown hair. Unlike the Mandrill, whose face is marked with brightly colored ridges, the Drill's face is solid, velvety black. More than a hundred years ago, when the animal was not very well known, scientists thought it was simply a young Mandrill and that as it grew older its face would take on the bright Mandril colors.

The Drill travels in large groups and feeds on vegetables, roots, insects, snakes, small animals and the like.

DUGONG

THE MARINE mammal known as the Dugong is believed to be (like its relative, the manatee) one of the creatures that gave rise to the ancient myth of the mermaid, half woman and half fish. However, it takes a good deal of imagination to see any resemblance to a human being in the Dugong's stubby muzzle, spindle-shaped body and blue-gray skin. The male, with its pair of short tusks, is certainly not feminine in appearance. The body (up to ten feet long) ends in crescent-shaped flukes which might, perhaps, be mistaken for the fish's tail mermaids were supposed to have.

The Dugong lives in shallow coastal waters of the Red Sea, along the east coast of Africa, and through the Indian Ocean to the Philippines and northern Australia. Comparatively little is known about its hab-its, but it is thought to be wholly vegetarian in its feeding and to "browse" on shallow-water marine plants. It is quite harmless, and is easily killed by spearing. Hunting is, in fact, so easy that the Dugong has diminished greatly in numbers and is in need of protection. Its meat is said to resemble pork or bacon and for a long time was rolled and smoked and sold in Australia as a substitute for bacon. An adult female will yield up to five or six gallons of oil, the inch-thick hide makes a good grade of leather, and even the bones were sometimes burned and used as charcoal in sugar-refining. These by-products are of minor importance, however, and Dugongs are usually killed only for the sake of their flesh.

The Dugong gives birth to one pup at a time and the gestation period is about one year.

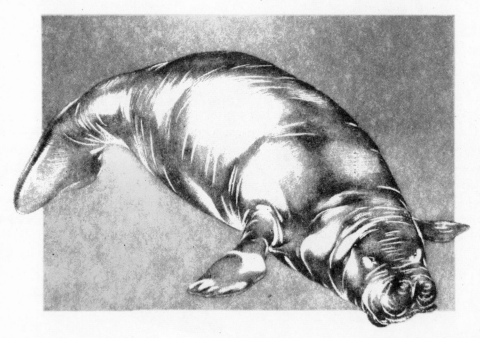

AMONG the dwarf antelopes of Africa, the Common Duiker is comparatively a giant, for it stands almost two feet high at the shoulders and its horns (which usually only the male carries) are as much as five inches long.

Duikers of various species are found all the way from the tropical parts of Africa down to the Cape. All of them are small; the Common Duiker is one of the medium-sized ones. Its body color is pale grayish-brown, more or less grizzled, with black hair on its throat and the underparts of its body.

'Duiker" is a Boer word meaning "diver," but in this case it does not mean that the Duikers dive into the water — rather, that they "dive" quickly into the bushes when they are alarmed.

Duikers travel singly or in pairs through brushy places, and when danger threatens, they dodge among the bushes, leaping over some and around others, so that they seem to be going in all directions at once. As soon as they reach a safe place, they stand up on their hind legs, look all around, and then start ducking and diving through the bushes again.

ECHIDNA

AUSTRALIA and New Guinea are the home of some of the world's strangest animals, and one of the queerest of them all is the Echidna, or Spiny Anteater. At first glance it looks something like a porcupine, for it has short, thick, yellowish spines all over its head and the upper part of its body. But it has a long snout, or beak, which does not resemble a porcupine at all.

What makes the Echidna especially peculiar is the fact that it lays eggs. There are only two kinds of mammals in the world that lay eggs, and the other is also found in Australia — the platypus, or duckbill. The platypus deposits its eggs in an underground nest, but the Echidna carries them in its pouch until they hatch.

When the baby Echidnas are hatched (there are usually two of them), they are nursed by their mother, just as other baby animals are nursed, for the Echidna is a true mammal even though it lays eggs.

One kind of Echidna is found in Australia, Tasmania and New Guinea, and it ranges in size from fifteen to twenty inches long. Another kind, called the Three-toed Echidna, lives in northwestern New Guinea and is considerably larger — about thirty inches long.

The Echidna sleeps in the daytime and comes out at night to hunt for nests of termites, which it licks up with its rough tongue. In the wild it is believed never to eat anything but ants, termites, or perhaps beetle grubs and other soft-bodied insects. Echidnas in the zoo live for many years on chopped meat, milk and eggs.

ALTHOUGH often called the "Indian Elephant," this great beast should be called the Asiatic Elephant because it is found in a wild state not only in India but in Assam, Burma, Ceylon, French Indo-China, the Malay Peninsula, Borneo and Sumatra. In all these regions large number of elephants have been domesticated and are used for heavy labor, such as timbering in jungle camps.

The elephants seen in circuses and zoological gardens are almost invariably the Asiatic form, not only because they are more easily obtained than African Elephants but because they are, generally, more tractable. Asiatic Elephants seem to take easily to domestication. Males are subject to period outbursts of dangerous rage, called "musth," and consequently females are more often exhibited than males.

Asiatic Elephants inhabit a great variety of terrain, from thick jungle to open, grassy plains. They wander in herds of ten to one hundred animals, feeding on grass and leaves; in some areas, wild elephants are a menace to cultivation and a herd may wreck a plantation in a single night. In captivity, a large elephant will eat about one hundred and fifty pounds of hay a day and drink fifty gallons of water.

ELEPHANT, AFRICAN

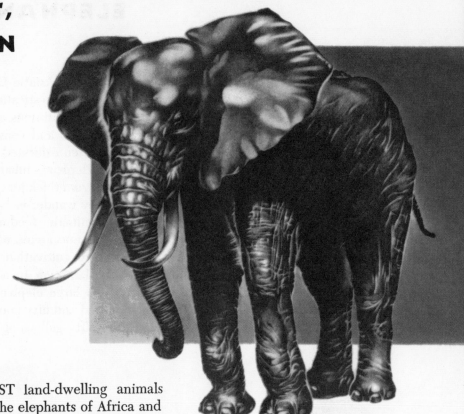

THE LARGEST land-dwelling animals alive today are the elephants of Africa and Asia. Generally speaking, the African Elephant is the taller, the Asiatic Elephant the bulkier.

Eleven feet is probably maximum height for any African Elephant alive today; 12,-000 pounds, or six tons, is near maximum weight.

The enormous ears, in height often half the standing height of the animal, are the most obvious characteristics of the African Elephant and enables one to distinguish it at a glance from the small-eared Asiatic.

The African Elephant has two "lips" on the end of its trunk and these are almost as useful as fingers. With its trunk an elephant pulls branches off trees, uproots grass, sprays its body with water and dust, tests uncertain ground, sniffs the air for the smell of enemies. It does not eat with its trunk, but merely uses the trunk as a hand and arm to stuff food into its mouth.

Elephants are comparatively plentiful today in a broad belt across the center of Africa. They live in the tropical forests, in grassy savannahs, in regions of grass and low bush. Cow elephants bear a single calf at a birth, after a gestation period of twenty-one to twenty-two months. The life span is not far below that of man — probably up to about sixty years.

ONE OF the great zoological rarities of the world is the civet-like Fossa of Madagascar. Its body is about two and a half feet long and its slender tail is almost as long; its appearance is weasel-like and its reputation quite as bloodthirsty as that of the weasel. Although it used to be fairly common, it is apparently disappearing, and it has been exhibited in zoological gardens only once or twice since it was first described by a naturalist more than a hundred years ago.

The Fossa is the largest carnivore, or meat-eater, in Madagascar. Its sleek hair is brown above and reddish-yellow below. Its sharp claws can be pulled into their sheaths, like the claws of a cat.

Naturalists do not agree on the ferocity of the Fossa, for although some say that when it gets into a poultry roost it will kill far more than it can eat, and that it will attack sheep and even young cattle, others think this is an exaggeration and that it is not really to be feared. However, the natives dislike it because, in parts of Madagascar where it is customary to seal the dead in caves, the Fossa sometimes digs out the corpses to feed upon them.

In the interior of Madagascar and in the great rain forests on the eastern coast of the island, black specimens of the Fossa have been reported.

FOX, ARCTIC

THERE ARE several kinds of these foxes, named after the regions in which they live — the Labrador Arctic Fox, the Pribilof Fox, and so on. Most of them turn white in winter to match the snow and ice, and brown or slate-color in summer. Some, however, known as "Blue" Foxes, stay smoky-gray or bluish all the year. These are not a different kind of fox, but simply a "color phase."

The open plains and the rocky hillsides where birds and small animals are plentiful are the home of the Arctic Fox in summertime. It will eat almost anything it can kill —even other Arctic Foxes if they are crippled or trapped. When food is plentiful, as when the lemmings swarm over the north-

land, the fox provides for the lean winter days by storing the bodies of its victims in crevices among the rocks. Despite the fact that it is quite at home on the ice, having thick, hairy pads on its feet to prevent slipping, the fox must have a hard time finding food in winter. It does not hibernate, or sleep through the winter months.

The skins of "Blue" Foxes are so valuable — they often bring $100 to $200 apiece — that Blues are raised for the fur market in fox farms on islands in the Bering sea.

The Arctic Fox is about thirty inches long (females are slightly smaller) and it averages around ten pounds in weight.

THE "SWIFT" is another name for the Kit Fox, and it describes this little animal well. Early naturalists, who saw it scurrying across the western plains, thought that it was the swiftest animal on the plains but more experience has taught us that the pronghorn "antelope" and perhaps some other foxes are faster — that, indeed, it can barely outrun a coyote.

It is the smallest of all the foxes in North America, being only a little more than two feet long and weighing about four and a half pounds. In fact, it is scarcely larger than a large house cat. Its general color is a pale, buffy-brown.

The Swift is a prairie animal and spends far more time in burrows than do other foxes. It seldom wanders from the shelter of a hole where it can take refuge. One such hole that was dug up was about nine feet long and the nest was five feet from the surface. Inside, in a nest lined with grass, were five puppies. The farmer who dug them out, took them home and reared them, but they never became really tame.

The Kit Fox feeds largely on such small prey as mice, prairie chickens, insects and the like. It is not very cunning, and many are killed by coyote traps or poisoned bait, which is a pity, for it is a harmless, attractive little creature. Its fur is not nearly so valuable as that of the Red Fox.

GEMSBOK

ALTHOUGH we are apt to think of Africa as a huge continent entirely covered with thick jungle, in reality it has vast areas of desert land and dry plains. These waste places are the home of the Oryx group of antelopes and one of the well-known species is the graceful, long-horned Gemsbok of South Africa.

It stands about four feet high, and its general body color is grayish. A dark stripe on the flanks divides the grayish upper part from the white of the underbody. It has spear-like horns about four feet long.

Explorers in Africa have often wondered how the Gemsbok manages to thrive on the open desert or among the low scrub where it would seem that even a locust could not find enough to eat. One traveler wrote: "Burning as is the climate, the Gemsbok is perfectly independent of water, which . . . I am convinced it never by any chance tastes."

The Gemsbok is not a fleet-footed animal, and even a hunter on foot can run it down. However, it is by no means defenseless or helpless, and can even beat off a lion with its horns. Skeletons of a lion and a Gemsbok have been found together, indicating that the Gemsbok stabbed the lion to death but was unable to withdraw its horns, so that both perished.

THE GIRAFFE, tallest of all living animals, has been known to reach a height of eighteen feet, but sixteen feet is the average of large adults. A baby Giraffe, born in the Bronx Zoo was five feet eight inches high at birth (the height of a medium-sized man) and weighed one hundred and ten pounds. A full-grown Giraffe may weigh 1000 to 1200 pounds. It can run astonishingly fast — up to thirty-two miles an hour.

The Giraffe is a browsing animal, feeding on the leaves of mimosa and acacia trees. It prefers to feed on high-growing leaves, but by spreading its front legs it can get its neck down and reach food near or on the ground. Incidentally, although the Giraffe has a very long neck, it has no more neck vertebrae than other mammals — seven. These bones are simply longer in the Giraffe.

In its hot, dry home in Africa, a Giraffe may go weeks or months without drinking water, getting all its moisture from the leaves it eats. In the zoo it drinks about two gallons a week. It is supposed to be a silent animal, but under certain circumstances it can make a mooing sound.

GIBBON

THE GORILLA, the Chimpanzee, the Orang-utan and the Gibbon are all called "anthropoid" apes — meaning "man-like" apes — because they are most like human beings in their skeletons, teeth, muscle arrangement and other physical characteristics. The Gibbon is generally considered the lowest of the anthropoid apes; in other words, it is the least man-like of the man-like forms.

There are several kinds of Gibbons and they are sometimes called by special names, such as the Siamang which lives in Sumatra, the White-handed Gibbon of the Malay Peninsula, and the Hoolock of Burma. They are all very much alike in their habits, and even in general appearance: they have extremely thin bodies, long arms that touch the ground when they stand upright, no tails, and bare, calloused places where they sit down. All of them spend most of their lives in the trees, although they can walk upright on the ground quite easily.

A Gibbon swinging through the trees seems to move without effort, hardly touching one limb before it is swinging and leaping to another. It can make jumps of forty feet, across and downward to another tree, without a moment's hesitation. Gibbons eat chiefly fruit and leaves, the tender shoots of plants, insects, spiders, bird's eggs and nestlings.

THE GNU is an antelope and there are several kinds that live in South and East Africa. The best-known are the White-tailed Gnu of South Africa and the Blue Gnu, or Brindled Gnu, of Central and East Africa. The White-tailed stands about forty-six inches high at the shoulder; the Brindled is a little larger.

So many of the antelopes are graceful, well-formed animals, that it is always sur-prising to think of the Gnu as an antelope. It really looks more like a horned horse. In color, all the Gnus are more or less the same —a dark, grayish-black — but the Blue Gnu really does have a kind of bluish tint in cer-tain lights.

Gnus are peculiar animals. They are the friskiest of all the antelopes and love to run, gallop, kick up their heels, snort and pre-tend to be furiously angry at everything. In-deed, they are apt to be dangerous, at least in zoos, and can seldom be trusted by their keepers.

They are familiar animals on the African plains, congregating in vast numbers around the waterholes with other antelopes, zebras and giraffes.

GORILLA

TWO KINDS of Gorillas live in Central Africa. One is called the Lowland Gorilla and it lives in the rain forests along the Equator near the Gulf of Guinea. The other is the Mountain Gorilla that lives near the eastern border of the Belgian Congo. About the only difference between them is that the Mountain Gorilla is generally a little larger and grows a longer and thicker coat of black hair.

Gorillas look as if they are very fierce. No doubt they are, if one went into a cage with full-grown Gorillas. But when they are babies, and even when old Gorillas are in their native jungles, they are almost always shy and inoffensive. They may attack men and other animals in order to protect themselves, but they do not kill animals in order to eat them. They eat only roots, vegetables, fruits and the like.

Gorillas travel in small family groups. At night they sometimes break branches and build little sleeping platforms on the ground or in a tree. Then they move on the next day and never use the same bed again. They can stand upright like a man, and babies often walk standing up, but older Gorillas always walk on all fours, their hands doubled up.

THE GNU is an antelope and there are several kinds that live in South and East Africa. The best-known are the White-tailed Gnu of South Africa and the Blue Gnu, or Brindled Gnu, of Central and East Africa. The White-tailed stands about forty-six inches high at the shoulder; the Brindled is a little larger.

So many of the antelopes are graceful, well-formed animals, that it is always surprising to think of the Gnu as an antelope. It really looks more like a horned horse. In color, all the Gnus are more or less the same —a dark, grayish-black — but the Blue Gnu really does have a kind of bluish tint in certain lights.

Gnus are peculiar animals. They are the friskiest of all the antelopes and love to run, gallop, kick up their heels, snort and pretend to be furiously angry at everything. Indeed, they are apt to be dangerous, at least in zoos, and can seldom be trusted by their keepers.

They are familiar animals on the African plains, congregating in vast numbers around the waterholes with other antelopes, zebras and giraffes.

GORILLA

TWO KINDS of Gorillas live in Central Africa. One is called the Lowland Gorilla and it lives in the rain forests along the Equator near the Gulf of Guinea. The other is the Mountain Gorilla that lives near the eastern border of the Belgian Congo. About the only difference between them is that the Mountain Gorilla is generally a little larger and grows a longer and thicker coat of black hair.

Gorillas look as if they are very fierce. No doubt they are, if one went into a cage with full-grown Gorillas. But when they are babies, and even when old Gorillas are in their native jungles, they are almost always shy and inoffensive. They may attack men and other animals in order to protect themselves, but they do not kill animals in order to eat them. They eat only roots, vegetables, fruits and the like.

Gorillas travel in small family groups. At night they sometimes break branches and build little sleeping platforms on the ground or in a tree. Then they move on the next day and never use the same bed again. They can stand upright like a man, and babies often walk standing up, but older Gorillas always walk on all fours, their hands doubled up.

MANY MILLIONS of years ago when animals, climate and even the shape of the continents were far different from what they are today, the members of the camel family lived in what is now the western part of the United States. As long periods of time passed, some of these moved to Asia by way of a "bridge" of land between Alaska and Asia, and others went down into South America.

Eventually all the camels died out in North America but they are still living as tame animals in Asia and northern Africa, and their South American relatives, the Guanaco and the vicuna, continue to exist.

The Guanaco, with its slender build and long neck, reminds one somewhat of a camel, but its ears are much longer in proportion to its size, its tail is short and bushy, it has no hump, and its brown coat is soft and woolly. It stands only three feet seven inches at the shoulder.

In some parts of South America the Guanaco is quite common and it is possible to see herds of a hundred or more. However, it is not a wary or cautious animal, and the Indians kill large numbers for the tasty meat and the soft skins, which make good rugs and saddle cloths.

GUENON

THERE ARE more than seventy kinds of monkeys called Guenons, and all of them live in Africa. Most of them are fond of "making faces," and their name of "Guenon" (pronounced "Gay-nun") is a French word for a person who grimaces, or makes a face.

To name just a few of the Guenons, there is the Green Monkey whose fur really is greenish yellow; the grizzled-gray Vervet Monkey; the Mona Monkey whose name of "Mona," in the Moorish language, means simply "Monkey," so that Mona Monkey is really "Monkey Monkey"; the Diana Monkey which has a beard and a white crescent on its forehead, like a new moon (the moon was the emblem of the goddess Diana); and the Hussar Monkey with red fur that reminds one of the red uniform of the Hussars.

Guenons are medium-sized monkeys, with long and slender tails which cannot be used for grasping. They are rather good-natured and friendly creatures, as a rule, and some of them used to be trained by organ-grinders to beg for pennies.

In Africa, the Guenons travel through the trees in separate families or in large droves, each under the leadership of an old "grandfather." Each drove seems to have its own particular part of the jungle and will fight other Guenons who trespass. Guenons are so fond of having their own little corner of the world that sometimes, when two of them share the same cage in a zoo, each will pick out his own corner and start a fight if the other comes near.

GUEREZA

AT ONE TIME, not so many years ago, it was fashionable for women to wear black-and-white capes of "monkey fur," and even to trim their hats and dresses with the fur. Almost always the skins of the Guereza, from tropical Africa, were used for these decorations.

Even longer ago — in fact, for hundreds of years in the past — the fierce soldiers of Abyssinia used that same kind of fur to decorate their war-shields.

It is easy to see why the fur was popular, for the Guereza is one of the prettiest of all the monkeys. Its body is about the size of a bulldog's and it is clothed in shiny black hair, rather long, with a mantle of long and pure white hair arising from the back and flowing down on both sides. Then, framing the animal's rather sad little face, there is a fringe of the same white hair. The top of the Guereza's head is black-haired, making it look like a white-whiskered old man with a black skull-cap.

Guerezas are quite rare in captivity, but a few have been exhibited in the Bronx Zoo in New York. In the wild they are supposed to spend the daylight hours gathering and eating leaves, wild fruits, seeds and insects, and then climbing to the top of the tallest trees to sleep in safety at night. In the zoo, however, they like green vegetables best.

HIPPOPOTAMUS, PIGMY

NO ONE in the world except a few explorers and the black natives of Western Africa had even seen a live Pigmy Hippopotamus until 1912. In that year an animal collector captured three of them and brought them back to the Bronx Zoo in New York.

For more than two hundred years explorers had told stories they had heard in Africa of the "big, black pig" that lived in the forests of what is now Liberia. Some people thought it was all imaginary, and others thought the Pigmy Hippopotamus would turn out to be just a baby hippopotamus of the big kind.

But when the three fat, black, greasy Pigmy Hippopotamuses came to America, everyone knew they were a new kind and different from any other animal that had been seen before. They were still very young, and weighed only about one hundred pounds each, but their heads were rounder and not as broad and. flat as the head of the other kind of hippopotamus. Besides, when they grew up, they only weighed about three hundred pounds, while the big hippopotamuses weighed more than fourteen times as much.

The Pigmy Hippopotamus lives in the thick jungles of Liberia, generally near streams and slow-flowing rivers. It likes the water, but when it is frightened it generally runs out on land. It sleeps in tunnels or sheltered places along the banks of the streams. It is a fierce animal, and in the zoo it often chases its keeper if he goes into its corral.

VARIOUS species of this small animal live in Africa, Arabia and Syria. It belongs in a zoological order and family by itself, but is so rodent-like in external appearance and habits that the Bible refers to it as the "Coney," a name that properly belongs to the rabbit. The structure of its teeth and feet relate it — distantly — to the rhineoceros and to the elephant.

A peculiarity of the Hyrax is a scent gland near the middle of its back. In one species this is nearly two inches long, and is surrounded by lighter-colored hairs. When the animal is frightened or irritated, these hairs rise and create a distinctive light spot.

Hyraces (the plural of Hyrax) live in large community groups, generally in rocky places, from sea level up to eleven thousand feet or higher, from South Africa north-ward to the highlands of Abyssinia. In the great equatorial rainforest, Tree Hyraces, differing slightly from the others in color and length of fur, live entirely in the trees instead of among rocks. All the Hyraces are mainly nocturnal, coming out at dusk to feed on leaves and young shoots. During the daytime they lie in the shade near some hole where they can take refuge at the slightest hint of danger.

The number of young at birth differs with the various species, but is usually three to six. The young are extremely playful and chase each other and their parents like kittens. An adult Hyrax is about the size of a rabbit and, until it was given protection by law in some parts of Africa, it was much hunted for the sake of its pelt, large numbers of which were sewn together to make robes or cushions.

IMPALA

ALMOST every explorer and hunter in Africa has a different idea as to which of the antelopes is the swiftest. Some of them claim that honor for the dark-reddish, slender-legged, long-horned Impala of southern and southeastern Africa.

One man tells of being in his camp one day when he heard a loud, rushing noise "coming on like a hurricane," and he looked up in time to see a pack of about twenty wild dogs pursuing a herd of Impalas.

"They passed our camp in fine style within a hundred yards of us," he wrote. "One of these animals cleared a distance of fifty feet in two successive bounds, and this on unfavorable ground, it being very soft and slippery."

If he actually measured the ground and found it to be fifty feet, that is certainly almost a record for the leap of an antelope.

The Impala stands about three feet high at the shoulder and its back and sides are dark red, which shades into white below. Its horns are twisted and backward and upward curving, and are most graceful. Some have been found as long as twenty-one inches.

This antelope seldom wanders very far from water, although it likes the low, sandy plains near a river where mimosa and scrub trees grow. It bounds away like an arrow from a bow when it is frightened, after making a sharp barking sound.

JACKAL

IN MANY stories about India and Africa, the Jackal is described as a mean and slinking animal, feeding on garbage and dead animals. Part of this description is certainly true, for it is not bold and it will eat nearly everything — refuse of all kinds, fruit, sugarcane, small animals, poultry and the like.

Jackals are relatives of the wolves, and there are several kinds of them. They live in the countries from southeastern Europe to India, and there are other kinds in north and south Africa. They are rather fox-like in appearance, with bushy tails, and are generally sandy-colored. Some have faint stripes. The Asiatic Jackal is about two and a half feet long, the African slightly larger.

The cry of a pack of Jackals is a fearsome thing. It is a long, wavering howl repeated three or four times, plus a series of quick yelps. Something about this ghostly cry makes it sound as if there were many more of the animals than actually are in the pack.

For more than two thousand years fables have been repeated in the countries around the Mediterranean, in which the Jackal plays the part of a scout, or spy, for lions and tigers. It is supposed to go ahead of these big animals and find food for them to kill, taking the scraps after they have eaten all they want. But that is just a fable.

JAGUAR

THE JAGUAR looks a great deal like the leopard, because both of them are big, yellowish cats with dark spots, called rosettes. There is one easily noticed difference—there is a black spot in the center of the Jaguar's rosettes. Otherwise they are much alike.

Nevertheless, they live a long distance apart — the leopard in Asia and Africa, and the Jaguar in South America, Central America and the southern part of North America. There are several kinds of Jaguars, and one of them is occasionally seen in Texas, New Mexico and Arizona. It is one of the smaller kinds, weighing only about two hundred pounds; some of those in South America weigh more than three hundred pounds.

The Jaguar is a bold animal and a dangerous hunter, for it kills cattle and there are reports that it will even go out of its way to attack human beings. Ranches in South America often employ hunters whose only job is to seek out and kill Jaguars which raid the herds of cattle. In the Spanish-speaking countries, the Jaguar is called "El Tigre," meaning "The Tiger."

"El Tigre" lives in thick jungle country. It can climb trees, but is more at home on the ground. Its voice is a hoarse, coughing sound, something like "uh, uh, uh, uh."

AUSTRALIA is the home of many of the world's queerest animals — the egg-laying platypus and echidna, for example — and in the Koala or so-called Native Bear it has one of the most appealing and attractive. The Koala is a "Teddy Bear" toy come to life.

Like most Australian mammals, it is a marsupial, or pouched, animal, with the odd circumstance that its pouch opens backward, toward the tail, rather than forward toward the head. Early settlers called it the Native Bear because of its vague general resemblance to a bear; actually it is in a zoological family by itself. The name Koala appears to come from a native word meaning "one who does not drink," for the animal seldom drinks water directly and seems to get enough moisture from dew and the eucalyptus leaves that are its sole natural diet.

The Koala in the wild feeds only on the leaves of gum, or eucalyptus, trees of about a dozen varieties. A single animal will eat about two and a half pounds of leaves a day. Koalas breed about every second year, and the embryo-like young, three-quarters of an inch long, is born after a gestation period thought to be of thirty-five days' duration. The baby is carried in the pouch for approximately two months and then emerges to ride on the mother's back, clinging tightly to her fur. An adult animal is about thirty inches long. Its life span is estimated to be a maximum of twenty years.

KANGAROO, GREAT GRAY

OF THE many kinds of kangaroos in Australia — the only part of the world where they are found — the largest is the Great Gray Kangaroo that may weigh as much as two hundred pounds, and measure about nine feet from nose to tail-tip. Some naturalists say it can jump at least twenty-six feet, and that it can easily leap over a fence four or five feet high. Ten and a half feet seems to be the record high jump for a 'roo.

Like most of the animals in Australia, the Kangaroo is a marsupial — that is, its babies are extremely tiny and undeveloped when they are born, and development takes place in the pouch in the mother's abdomen. The baby of a Great Gray Kangaroo, for instance, is only about an inch long and is only one three-thousandths of the weight of its mother. Human babies at birth are about one twentieth of the mother's weight.

As soon as it is born, the baby Kangaroo crawls through the mother's fur into the pouch and takes hold of the nipple with its mouth. It stays in the pouch until it is five or six months old. Then it may put its head out for the first time, and in a few more weeks it comes entirely out of the pouch and hops around. For many weeks after that, until it grows too large, it hops back in again when it is hungry or tired or frightened.

The Kangaroo generally has only one baby at a time. Its life span is believed to be ten or fifteen years. Most species feed chiefly on grass, and Australian farmers blame them for destroying grazing areas, although they certainly do not do a great deal of damage.

SOUTHEASTERN Asia is the home of several species of monkey known as Langurs. One of the best-known is the Hanuman Langur of central and northern India, for it has for centuries been held sacred by the Hindus and allowed to wander into their bazaars and shops and to steal grain or anything else it wanted. Its common name comes from the Hindu diety Hanuman, to whom the monkey is sacred.

The Hanuman is a rather large monkey, up to two and a half feet long, with a tail that may measure more than three feet in length. It travels in troops, old and young, males and females, and in the early morning and late evening the forest echoes with their whooping calls. In their native forests they feed on leaves and the young shoots of trees, but when they raid a village they show a fondness for grain.

The whooping cry of the Langur has at times been of service to tiger-hunters, for a Langur, seeing a tiger slinking through the underbrush, will follow it — swinging through the treetops — and keep up a running cry that warns the hunter exactly where the tiger is.

Although the Hanuman and most other Langurs, including those of Madras, Ceylon and the Malabar coast, are denizens of the steaming tropical jungles, one species lives in the Himalayas and is found at elevations of 5000 to 12,000 feet, among snow-clad trees.

LEMMING

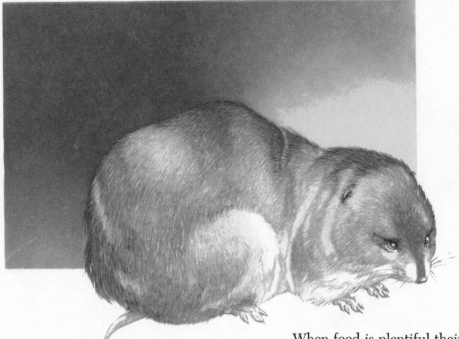

ONE OF the wonders of the animal world is the migration of the Lemmings on the Scandinavian peninsula—a journey that for some of them ends only when they plunge into the sea and swim until they are exhausted.

Lemmings are rodents, or gnawing animals, closely related to the rats and mice. The so-called Norway Lemming is one whose long journeys are best known, but the Lemmings of Arctic North America also sometimes makes similar migrations. All Lemmings feed on vegetable matter—grass, moss, lichens, the leaves of the stunted plants that grow in the far North.

When food is plentiful their numbers increase enormously, all out of proportion to the available food supply. Then they start to migrate to new territory and vast hordes swarm down the mountains onto the plains and travel through swamps and cities, across rivers and lakes, stopping for no obstacles. The more persistent Lemmings continue until they reach the sea. To them it is no doubt only another body of water to be crossed, with greener pastures beyond. Eventually they sink beneath the waves.

The Norwegian Lemming is about five inches long, yellowish-brown, spotted and streaked with brown. The American Lemming, about six inches long over-all, is grizzled buffy, grayish and black on the head and upper back, reddish on the lower back.

HUMAN beings and apes and monkeys all belong in one big group of animals that naturalists call "Primates." At the top of the group are people — man — and at the bottom are the little creatures with fox-like, blank-expressioned faces that are called Lemurs. Most of them live on the great island of Madagascar on the east side of Africa.

They are queer little things, the largest only about two feet long. They move about mostly at night and they are usually stealthy in their movements. That is perhaps why the great naturalist Linnæus, who named them, gave them the name "Lemur," which comes from a Latin word that the ancient Romans used when they spoke of bad spirits of the dead.

Lemurs spend almost all their lives in trees and only come down to the ground when they have to, to get water or to reach another tree. They eat fruits and leaves and insects, snakes, birds, eggs, and almost anything they can find in the trees.

Many native peoples are afraid of the Lemurs because of the blank, expressionless look on their faces, but they are really quite harmless little things and can easily be tamed.

Some Lemurs have tails, others do not. Even the ones with very long tails cannot hold on with them, as some South American monkeys can.

LEOPARD

BIG, SPOTTED cats known as Leopards are found all through Africa and Asia. Some live high in the Himalayas among the ice and snow — a strange place to find animals we usually think of as loving warmth and sunshine.

The Leopard looks a great deal like the jaguar of the American tropics, for they are similarly spotted. The Leopard, however, is generally slimmer than the jaguar. It varies a great deal in size and while some are only about five feet long, others are truly big cats eight feet long.

Most of us know only the yellowish Leopard, spotted with black, but there is a Black Leopard that is black all over without any yellow. Nevertheless, the spots that make the ordinary yellowish Leopard so striking have not entirely disappeared, and in certain lights it is possible to see "blacker" black spots on the Black Leopard's fur. This Black Leopard is what is called a "color phase" of the ordinary Leopard — not a separate species. Both black and spotted cubs may be born in the same litter.

Leopards are very active animals. They climb trees as easily as monkeys and can leap from bough to bough or spring on an unsuspecting animal with great ferocity and quickness — with even more ferocity than a tiger. In India Leopards often lurk in the neighborhood of native villages, waiting a chance to spring on a dog or a goat or a calf. Occasionally an individual Leopard becomes a man-killer, but as a rule they attack only wild game and domestic animals.

THE COMMON names of animals often refer to some peculiarity of their appearance, and this is the case with the Clouded Leopard. "Clouded" refers to the rather large, irregular, dark blotches on the grayish-brown fur of the animal. In many kinds of spotted wild cats, the dark spots are sharp and regular in shape, but in the Clouded Leopard of southeastern Asia, Formosa, Sumatra, Java and Borneo the cloudy dark gray patches are so numerous that the lighter base color of the animal is reduced to narrow streaks or bands.

The Malay name for the animal is equally descriptive; they call it the Rimau-dahan, or "Tiger of the Trees." It is a forest-dwelling animal, and spends much of its life actually in the trees, even sleeping curled up in a forked branch. While it may hunt on the ground, there is usually plenty of food to be found in the trees — birds and small mammals that climb the trees in search of their own food.

This is one of the larger wild cats, with a head and body length of about three and a half feet. Its tail is longer than that of the common leopard, about two and a half feet. Its upper canine teeth are proportionately longer than those of any other cat animal.

Because it is primarily a forest-dwelling animal, the Clouded Leopard is not the menace to native livestock that some of the other big cats, particularly the common leopard, often are.

LION

IN FABLES and stories, the Lion is the "King of Beasts," the noblest and most powerful of all the animals. It is indeed true that a full-grown male Lion, fully ten feet long from his nose to the end of his tail, with a great ruff of hair around his neck and his tawny yellow body crouched to spring, is a striking picture of strength and ferocity. Such a Lion might weigh five hundred pounds.

All of Africa is the home of the Lion, although it has been killed off in many parts and now is commonest in the large wild game preserves. At one time it ranged eastward to western India, but only a few are left there, in the wilder parts.

The Lion likes open country — the treeless, grassy plains where there are plenty of zebras and antelopes and smaller game on which it can feed. One of its favorite methods of getting food is to lurk near a water hole where other animals come to drink.

It hunts mostly at night, and sleeps by day in reeds or thickets. Sometimes Lions hunt alone, sometimes in small parties of four or five. Their roars as they call to each other during the night are like rumblings of distant thunder.

Only the male Lions have manes of hair on their necks and shoulders, and in Africa these are seldom as long and bushy as on Lions in captivity. Lionesses have as many as six cubs at a birth. The babies are born with their eyes shut; they open in about a week.

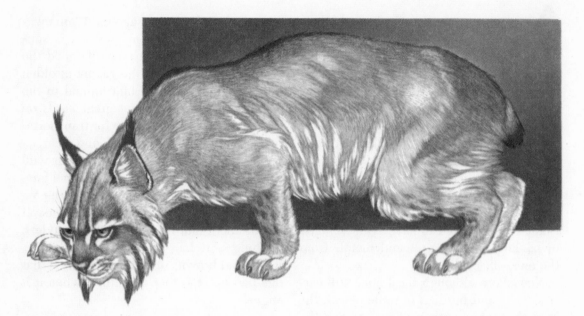

THE LYNX is a hunter of hares and rabbits, of foxes, young deer and even of mountain sheep, in the heavily-forested northern parts of North America. It ranges all the way south from Alaska through Canada to Pennsylvania, and westward into Oregon and the mountains of Colorado. Still further south there is a more reddish-colored close relative known as the Bobcat, Wildcat or Bay Lynx.

Naturalists have sometimes compared the Canada Lynx to a house cat, for it does look somewhat like an overgrown house cat and its series of mewing, yowling, caterwauling calls is very reminiscent of "alley cat" concerts. But there are many real differences besides size. The Lynx has a very short tail,

its ears are strongly tufted, it does not mind swimming, and it is an efficient killer of fairly sizeable game. Male Lynxes are larger than females, and a good-sized male is thirty-six to thirty-nine inches long from the nose to the end of the four inch tail. The largest one on record weighed forty-four pounds.

Few persons have ever seen a Lynx in the wild because it prowls mostly at night and almost always keeps to the thick woods. It does not hibernate, or go into a long winter sleep; its broad feet enable it to travel on top of the snow and hunt game that flounders and sinks in the drifts.

One to four baby Lynxes are born in the spring, generally in a hollow log or in a hole among rocks.

LLAMA

AT THE time the Spaniards made their conquest of parts of South America about three hundred fifty years ago, the natives of Peru used the Llama as a beast of burden very much as we use a horse or a mule, or as the people of the Arctic regions today use the reindeer. Old accounts tell of droves of three hundred to a thousand Llamas travelling along the mountain paths under the charge of a single driver and each animal carrying a heavy silver ingot from the fabulously wealthy mines. At one time 300,000 Llamas are believed to have been engaged in hauling precious ores and metals from the mines in Peru.

Nowadays, although the Llama still carries riders and burdens in some places, the horse has taken over in many parts of the Andes.

Nobody knows how many hundreds or even thousands of years ago the Llama was domesticated. Its ancient ancestor is supposed to be the Guanaco — still called the Wild Llama. Certainly the Llama in olden times was a most important animal to the people of Peru. They kept great herds on the mountain pastures, some for transportation and others to furnish milk and meat.

The Llama is the largest of the four wild or domesticated members of the camel family in South America — the Alpaca, the Vicuna and the Guanaco are the others. It stands about four feet high at the shoulders. Its long, soft hair may be brown, white, white-and-brown, or almost black. It has one bad habit — that of spitting when it is angry.

THE DUTCH colonists of the East Indian islands are responsible for the name of the Slow Loris. Their word "loeris" means "a clown," and it is a pretty good description of this little animal, about the size of a cat, that lives in Assam, Indo-China and Malaysia. The natives of India have another descriptive name for it. They call it "Sharmindi billi," which means "the bashful cat."

It *does* act as if it were bashful or embarrassed, for much of the time it creeps through the trees with its head tucked down as if it were ashamed to look at anyone.

The Slow Loris is really slow. It spends almost all its life in the trees, never coming to the ground unless it has to, and it climbs up, down and across the interlacing limbs of the jungle trees as if it had a whole lifetime to reach the hole in some hollow tree where it curls up to sleep through the daytime. At dusk it uncurls and begins a slow prowl in search of leaves and tender twigs, fruits, insects and birds.

This little animal and its relative, the Potto of Africa, belong to a family which is the lowest of the monkey group. It does not look very much like a monkey — actually it looks more like some strange little cat. Its grayish-brown hair is long and soft and wooly, with a dark stripe down the back. Like many animals that hunt at night, the Loris has very large eyes.

MACAQUE, PIG-TAILED

IN ASIA there is one rather large group of monkeys known as Macaques. Various kinds live in India, Burma, the Malay Peninsula, Borneo, Sumatra, parts of China and Japan. One of the most familiar ones, because it is frequently seen in zoos, is the Pig-tailed Macaque of southeastern Asia.

There is no doubt about it being well named, for it comes pretty close to having no tail at all — just a thin, short, curling tail so much like a pig's that one almost expects the monkey to grunt! Some of the Macaques actually do not have tails, while others have quite long ones. They are not prehensile, or grasping tails; only the monkeys of the New World have those.

Macaques travel together in large troops. They roam through the jungles, eating insects and seeds and fruits and even lizards. Whenever they find more food than they can eat at the moment, they stuff the excess into their large cheek-pouches, to be eaten later.

A long time ago a great naturalist told of seeing Pig-tailed Macaques on the island of Sumatra that had been trained to run up cocoanut palms, pull off the ripe cocoanuts, and throw them down to their masters. If this story is true, the monkeys must have been very young ones, or females, for the old males are fierce and vicious and certainly could not be trained to be so useful.

MANY KINDS of monkeys do not have the ability to make a variety of "faces." They are apt to have only about two expressions — one, just a quiet, vacant expression, when they are not thinking about anything in particular; the other, a "face" that expresses anger or fear.

But the Mangabeys of West Africa are noted for their expressive faces and to see them scowl, and grimace, and curl their lips as if they were smiling, all the while winking their white eyelids and chattering in many different tones, one would be sure that they were holding a most interesting conversation among themselves.

The Sooty Mangabey, whose body is dull black with an ashy color underneath, and the White-collared Mangabey that is blackish-gray with a band of white fur around its neck, are most commonly seen in zoological gardens. Both of them have long tails, which they carry turned forward over the back.

Mangabeys are often good-natured and friendly monkeys. For many years one lived in the London Zoo. It learned to perform many amusing tricks, such as turning somersaults and dancing, in order to beg peanuts from visitors. It liked to be petted, too, and would seize a visitor's hand in its paws, turn it over and examine it carefully, and all the while show how pleased it was by smacking its lips and making low, grunting sounds.

MANDRILL

OF ALL the baboons — none of which are handsome — the Mandrill of West Africa is certainly the fiercest-looking. And an old male, at least, is just as fierce as it looks.

Indeed, one naturalist said of the Mandrill: "Its whole appearance is far more suggestive of the forms imagined during a nightmare than is the case with any other living Mammals."

This baboon has a stout, chunky body clothed in blackish-olive fur, but the things everyone notices at once are the bright colors at its either end. Its tail is very short and is surrounded by a large patch of bare skin that is bright red! At the other end of the animal, its face has a series of large, ridge-like swellings on either side of the nose, and these ridges are blue, purple, red and Chinese white.

Such a color scheme may sound quite attractive, but the general effect of the animal is not, for it has deep-set eyes and heavy, projecting eyebrows that give its face a scowling and ferocious appearance. Being such a large animal — about the size of a collie dog although heavier of body — it looks as dangerous as it is.

The Mandrill travels in large troops in country that is rocky and broken, feeding on roots, vegetables, insects, small animals —in fact, almost anything it can find.

MARMOSET

THE SMALLEST monkey in the world is one of the Marmosets — the Pigmy Marmoset of Brazil that is so small it can curl up comfortably in a girl's hand. It weighs only about four and a half ounces.

The great jungles of Brazil are the home of most of the Marmosets. Almost all of them are smaller than a squirrel, with long tails that are usually ringed with bands of light and dark hair. These tails are not prehensile, or grasping. Several of the Marmosets have fluffs of long hair around their ears. Marmosets are tree-dwelling monkeys and leap from branch to branch with great ease as they search for fruit and insects. They have high, squeaky voices.

One of the prettiest of them is the Lion Marmoset of southeastern Brazil. It is a beautiful golden color, with long and flowing hair. In captivity both the father and the mother take turns in caring for the babies, the father carrying them on his back until feeding time. Then he turns them over to the mother, who carries them a while and finally gives them back to the father. The babies grow rapidly and in a little more than six months are as large as their parents.

MARTEN

THE RESTLESS Marten, small relative of the fisher and a member of the Weasel family, never seems to grow tired. In the wild it is ceaselessly on the go, leaping from branch to branch, up and down the tree, always in a hurry and seemingly never stopping to catch its breath.

Squirrels are part of its food — it catches chipmunks, mice, rabbits, frogs and snakes, too, and is said to be fond of the orange berries of the mountain ash — and any animal that can catch a squirrel in a tree *has* to be fast and active.

The various kinds of Martens are found through the forested parts of North America all the way across the continent. The deeper, thicker the woods, the better the Marten likes them. It is a secretive animal and only an occasional trapper or expert woodsman is ever likely to see one in the forests, for the Marten departs for still deeper woods as soon as clearings are made and houses are built.

The rich, yellowish-brown fur of the Marten is valuable and it is eagerly sought by trappers. It is easy to trap. Shy as it is, it is unsuspicious of traps and quite ready to attack the bait. The Marten hunts both by day and by night. Some naturalists believe that it stores up food for "a rainy day" — burying what is left over after it has eaten all it can hold.

THE SMALLEST monkey in the world is one of the Marmosets — the Pigmy Marmoset of Brazil that is so small it can curl up comfortably in a girl's hand. It weighs only about four and a half ounces.

The great jungles of Brazil are the home of most of the Marmosets. Almost all of them are smaller than a squirrel, with long tails that are usually ringed with bands of light and dark hair. These tails are not prehensile, or grasping. Several of the Marmosets have fluffs of long hair around their ears. Marmosets are tree-dwelling monkeys and leap from branch to branch with great ease as they search for fruit and insects. They have high, squeaky voices.

One of the prettiest of them is the Lion Marmoset of southeastern Brazil. It is a beautiful golden color, with long and flowing hair. In captivity both the father and the mother take turns in caring for the babies, the father carrying them on his back until feeding time. Then he turns them over to the mother, who carries them a while and finally gives them back to the father. The babies grow rapidly and in a little more than six months are as large as their parents.

MARTEN

THE RESTLESS Marten, small relative of the fisher and a member of the Weasel family, never seems to grow tired. In the wild it is ceaselessly on the go, leaping from branch to branch, up and down the tree, always in a hurry and seemingly never stopping to catch its breath.

Squirrels are part of its food — it catches chipmunks, mice, rabbits, frogs and snakes, too, and is said to be fond of the orange berries of the mountain ash — and any animal that can catch a squirrel in a tree *has* to be fast and active.

The various kinds of Martens are found through the forested parts of North America all the way across the continent. The deeper, thicker the woods, the better the Marten likes them. It is a secretive animal and only an occasional trapper or expert woodsman is ever likely to see one in the forests, for the Marten departs for still deeper woods as soon as clearings are made and houses are built.

The rich, yellowish-brown fur of the Marten is valuable and it is eagerly sought by trappers. It is easy to trap. Shy as it is, it is unsuspicious of traps and quite ready to attack the bait. The Marten hunts both by day and by night. Some naturalists believe that it stores up food for "a rainy day" — burying what is left over after it has eaten all it can hold.

THE SOUTH AFRICAN veldt is the home of the Meerkat, a rather slender-bodied member of the mongoose family. Here it lives in burrows, often large numbers of animals in the same area, and it has the prairie dog-like habit of sitting upright in front of its burrow basking in the sun. It pops underground instantly if an intruder comes too near.

The animal's body is about twelve inches long, and its thick, soft fur is grizzled gray, with darker stripes crossing the hinder part of the back. Like all its relatives — which include civets, genets and the true mongooses — the Meerkat has a sharp, bright, inquisitive face and its actions are quick and abrupt.

Insects probably form the bulk of its food, although, mongoose-like, it takes eggs, young snakes, mice, nestling birds, or almost anything else it can get. It even eats the bulbs of plants. It is reported to have a great liking for dogs, often trotting after them for great distances.

Because of its relationship to the Indian mongoose, which has caused serious depredations among poultry in the West Indian islands where it has been introduced, the Meerkat is not permitted to enter the United States. The few specimens that have been seen in American zoological gardens were brought in under special permit.

MONKEY, LION-TAILED

WESTERN India is the home of one of the world's most attractive monkeys — the Lion-tailed Monkey that has an enormous ruff of gray hair around its black face. Its common name comes from the fact that its rather long and slender tail ends in a fluffy, bushy tuft like a lion's tail.

The fur that covers the animal's body is long and shining black, which emphasizes the gray "beard" around its face.

This is one of the group of Old World monkeys known as macaques, which are found in Africa, Asia and Malaysia. Most of them have elastic cheek-pouches and can store enormous quantities of food there, un- til their faces bulge to almost twice their normal size. After stuffing their cheeks as fast as they can, they bring the food out a little at a time and eat it.

The Lion-tailed Monkey lives in forested uplands, travelling in small parties of a dozen to twenty individuals. It is a shy and wary monkey, keeping high in the trees and making off at the approach of hunters. Although natives are generally good at taming monkeys and keeping them in captivity, the Lion-tailed Monkey is likely to turn savage and morose when it is taken out of its forest home.

"PROBOSCIS" is a dictionary word for a nose. Just one glance at the picture of a Proboscis Monkey shows why it was named that.

The Proboscis Monkey has the longest nose of any of the monkeys — indeed, many monkeys have almost no nose at all; at least, not one that extends out from the face—and scientists are puzzled as to why it should have such an enormous proboscis, for it does not seem to be of any particular use to the animal.

More than one hundred and fifty years ago, when the first Proboscis Monkey of Borneo was described by a naturalist, he said that the natives told him that when a Proboscis Monkey jumps from one tree to another, it always holds its nose with one hand.

However, that seems to be just a story, for naturalists have seen many Proboscis Monkeys jumping, and they never held their noses—they simply jumped, with their arms and legs outstretched.

It is a large monkey, with a head and body about thirty inches long and a tail more than two feet long. Its hair is yellowish and around the bare skin of its face there is a fringe of different-colored hair.

MONGOOSE

MONKEY

MONGOOSES (the plural is not "Mongeese") are found in many parts of Africa, India and Malaya, and have been introduced into some other areas, particularly the West Indies and Hawaii, because of their reputation as killers of rats and poisonous snakes.

Typically, all the Mongooses have long, slender, weasel-like bodies, rather long tails, grizzled fur and rather pointed heads. The Indian Mongoose is gray or brownish-gray in color and its head and body are fifteen to eighteen inches long, with a tail about fourteen inches long. It is an open-country animal, likely to be found in thickets, among cultivated fields or in broken, bushy ground — places where it can find its favorite food of mice, snakes, lizards, small birds, eggs and insects.

There is no evidence that the Mongoose is an especial enemy of the cobra or any other poisonous snake and it is not true that if bitten, it eats the leaves of a jungle plant and is not affected by the venom.

Mongooses are not allowed to enter the United States. They became a pest in the West Indies, where they were introduced to kill the poisonous fer-de-lance. Although they killed some snakes, they took a liking to birds, poultry and other small mammals and did considerable harm.

IN THE vast jungles of South and Central America the whoops and groans and growls of the Howler Monkeys are as familiar to the natives as the "beep-beep" of automobile horns are to us. For the Howler has a powerful voice and likes to use it. Sitting alone in the top of some gigantic tree, a Howler will often let out a series of calls that — unless you knew better — would make you think a whole troop of monkeys was being eaten alive by jaguars.

The Howler is able to produce such a resonant sound because of a peculiar hollow shell of bone on the upper part of its windpipe.

There are several kinds of Howlers — the Red Howler, the Black Howler, and so on — but they are all jungle-dwellers in the hottest parts of the American tropics. Brazil is the home of many of them. They are medium-sized monkeys, with grasping tails, and are mostly tree-dwellers. They are supposed to eat very little except leaves.

MONKEY, RHESUS

EVERY year thousands of Rhesus Monkeys are brought to the United States from India to be sold to zoos that have "monkey islands," or to be used in medical research in hospitals. So many are imported that it would almost seem that the supply could not last very much longer — but still the great troops of these noisy, quarrelsome, lively little monkeys swarm through the jungles of India.

The Rhesus belongs to the group of Asiatic monkeys known as macaques. The Hindus of India call it the "Bandar."

Few monkeys are as amusing to watch as a large family of Rhesus, consisting perhaps of a large, grave, short-tempered old grandfather, some large males and females, and a whole troop of babies and youngsters. They seldom stand still for more than a moment and are continually chasing each other, chattering and screeching when tempers flare up, or when one mother thinks that some other monkey is going to harm her baby. Then, a moment later, they forget all about being angry, and calmly sit down and groom each other's fur. A Rhesus baby is a tiny little thing, almost hairless.

The Rhesus Monkey is not afraid of water, as so many monkeys are, and even seems to enjoy getting wet. It is a good swimmer.

A GREAT NATURALIST once said that the Squirrel Monkey's face looks more like that of a little child than of any other monkey he knew. He said that it could look as innocent as a child, and smile like a child, and that when it is afraid, its big eyes fill with tears.

The Squirrel Monkey (sometimes called the Moss Monkey because of its greenish hair) lives in South America. It is hardly larger than a squirrel, although it has an extremely long, slender tail.

The Indians of Brazil say that when a hard rain comes, a number of these little monkeys will huddle close together on the branch of a tree, their tails twined around their necks, for the sake of keeping each other warm. Sometimes ten or twelve will crowd together, while others that cannot find room on the limb will stand nearby and make mournful sounds because they are kept out of the huddle.

It makes an excellent pet and many an Indian family, living far back in the jungle, keeps a young Squirrel Monkey tethered around its palm-thatched hut. Monkeys that have been brought up with human beings in this way often develop a habit of watching the mouth of a person when he is speaking, and they like to reach out and touch the lips of a speaker.

The Squirrel Monkey travels in rather large groups, hunting fruits and insects and probably young birds in the trees.

MONKEY, SPIDER

THE SPIDER MONKEY gets its name from its very long, "spiderlike" arms and legs. Even a well-fed adult Spider Monkey, clothed in its coarse black or grayish-brown hair, looks thin and frail — as if it hadn't had a square meal for weeks.

On one occasion the Bronx Zoo received a Spider Monkey that was suffering from a skin disease and it was necessary to clip all the animal's fur off close to the body. The result was a walking skeleton — or what appeared to be one. The little animal had been well fed and its body was actually "plump," by Spider Monkey standards, but it was so naturally thin that the Veterinarian kept it carefully concealed until its hair grew out again, for fear people would think the zoo was underfeeding its animals.

Spider Monkeys of various kinds live all through the American tropics, from Central America well down into South America. They are tree-dwelling monkeys, with strong prehensile tails by which they can actually hang and swing back and forth while their hands and feet are occupied with stuffing fruits and berries into their mouths.

Some Indians in South America eat Spider Monkeys — as well as other kinds of monkeys. They sometimes shoot them with arrows tipped with a weak poison that kills the animal but does not harm people who eat the meat.

TWO ISLANDS in the Mediterranean, Sardinia and Corsica, are the only places where the Mouflon is found. It is a rather small wild sheep, standing only about twenty-seven inches at the shoulder, but its body is neat and compact, and its short hair of reddish-brown on the upper part of the body, together with its broad and forward-sweeping horns, give it a handsome appearance.

The Mouflon is supposed to be closely related to our domestic sheep, for there are accounts of wild Mouflon that occasionally desert the flocks of their own kind, and go live with the tame sheep in the valleys of the islands. Furthermore, a domestic lamb that has lost its mother sometimes joins a flock of Mouflon.

In Sardinia, the Mouflon lives on the highest ridges of certain of the mountain chains and generally the old rams pick out spots from which they can see out over all the surrounding country. Here, in the shade of a low bush, they stand watch while the flock grazes.

The old rams engage in fierce battles at mating time, butting with their heavy horns. The lambs are born in the early spring and in a few days are strong enough to follow their mothers everywhere.

NYALA

IN ZULULAND and Nyasaland in Africa there are vast areas where small, bush-like trees grow thick and close and where it is almost impossible for a man to travel unless he follows the narrow trails worn by the feet of animals. Here is the home of the handsome antelope known as the Nyala, or Inyala.

There are many kinds of antelopes, and some of them have white stripes on their bodies — stripes that look a little like harness. Thus they are called the "Harnessed Antelopes." The Nyala is one of this group. It is a medium-sized antelope, about three and a half feet tall at the shoulder, and it is slender and graceful. The male has a slate gray body and brown legs, with a fringe of long hair that runs down its throat and under its body. There is another fringe of hair on its back.

The male has a handsome pair of curved horns, too, while his mate has no horns, no fringe of hair, and is quite a different color — a beautiful mahogany red.

In its native bush, the Nyala travels in small groups, browsing on leaves and shrubs and fruit. Many antelopes exist in huge numbers, but the Nyala is a comparatively scarce animal and its numbers have been further reduced by native meat-hunters, hoof-and-mouth disease, and campaigns to destroy game that may carry the sleeping sickness. Leopards and hunting dogs also take their toll, so that this beautiful antelope has been placed under strict international protection since 1933.

"LITTLE JAGUAR," the Ocelot has sometimes been called, for it is a medium-sized, spotted cat of the tropical parts of the New World, ranging over about the same territory as the much larger jaguar. Tiger-cat and Leopard-cat are other well-known names for it. Most of the various kinds of Ocelot are found in Central and South America, but one form is occasionally seen in southwestern Texas.

A male Ocelot is a little more than four feet long from the tip of its nose to the end of its tail. Females are about ten inches shorter. The average weight is twenty-five to thirty-five pounds.

Like many of the other cats, the Ocelot prefers to hunt its food at night. During the daytime it sleeps in thickets, coming out at dusk to make long rambles through the forest and underbrush in search of birds, rabbits, wood rats, mice, snakes and such small game. The subspecies that is found in Texas has a bad habit of making raids on poultry houses, catching chickens on their roosts. In the main, however, it is not a troublesome animal, for by far the greater number live in wild jungle areas where they come into slight contact with man.

In disposition, the Ocelot is unusually mild for a wild member of the cat family, and baby Ocelots are often sold as pets in South American ports. There are few breeding records on the animal, but apparently it has two young in a litter, and they are born in mid-autumn.

OKAPI

In THE year 1900 Sir Harry Johnston, a British official carrying out a mission in the Congo, noticed that one of his native soldiers carried his gun slung from a strip of reddish-brown and white hide. Sir Harry had never seen any animal with exactly that color and shade of markings, so he bought the hide and began to make inquiries about the animal. The natives knew it well enough; they called it "Okapi" in their dialect.

Naturalists in London at first thought it might have come from some hitherto undiscovered species of forest-dwelling zebra, but some time later Sir Harry managed to find a whole skin and a skull of an Okapi and then it was realized that this was an entirely different kind of animal — not a zebra at all.

They named it Okapi in English, adopting the name used in the Belgian Congo, and after long investigation decided the animal was more closely related to the giraffe than to any other animal in the world today. The Okapi has changed very little from its ancestors which lived about thirty million years ago, and so it is a true "living fossil."

The Okapi dwells in the deepest, darkest jungle. It has a long neck, although not nearly as extreme as a giraffe's, and its tongue is so long that it can reach out and lick its own ears.

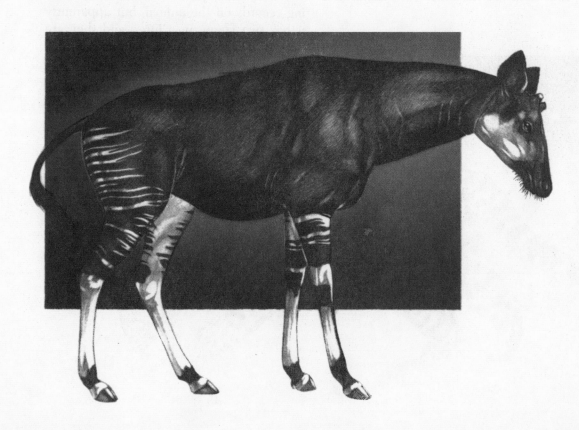

"ORANG-UTAN" is a Malay word meaning "Man-of-the-Woods" — a descriptive term, for this huge anthropoid (or man-like) ape is most at home in the trees of its native Borneo and Sumatra. On the ground it walks upright, its arms dangling and its fingers almost touching the ground. Although an adult stands only about four to four and a half feet tall, its outstretched arms may have a reach of more than seven and a half feet. A big male weighs more than two hundred pounds.

The jungle home of the Orang-utan is one of the thickest and most luxuriant in the world. Being almost entirely a tree-dweller, the Orang seldom has occasion to come to the ground, and can proceed for great distances by swinging from one tree to another. It is never in a hurry, and many small monkeys are; it moves slowly and deliberately. Nevertheless, it can work through the trees as fast as a man can run on the ground below.

Orangs usually travel in small family parties, feeding as they go on leaves and buds and young shoots. The prickly fruit of the durian is one of their favorite foods.

OTTER, SEA

THIS GRACEFUL animal whose pelt is so highly prized in the fur trade, has been almost exterminated from the North Pacific coast although in recent years it has been increasing in numbers under strict government protection.

As Otters go, it is rather large — about three feet long in head and body, with a tail a foot long. Its sleek fur is dark brown, its hind feet are long and broad and webbed and have furry soles. Its feet resemble the flippers of a seal and enable the animal to slide through the water with astonishing ease and speed.

The Sea Otter is known to exist still in certain parts of the Alaskan coast and near Monterey, California. It lives in and around the beds of kelp, or seaweed, on which it is said to feed at times. Mussels, cuttlefish and sea urchins, however, are its usual diet. Abalones are a favorite food. It is clever enough to smack two clams together so as to break the hard shells and get at the soft edible parts. The Sea Otter is known to dive to depths of three hundred feet in search of food.

One or sometimes two young are born and the mother is playful and affectionate with them. There are stories that she even sleeps in the water, on her back, with a baby clasped to her breast.

Russian sealers hunted the Sea Otter so ruthlessly during the past 150 years that it was almost gone from Alaskan waters when the United States Government in 1910 passed a law protecting it. At that time Sea Otter skins were selling for $1,000 apiece.

UNTIL A FEW years ago practically no-body except naturalists had ever heard of the Giant Panda, but today children all over the United States play with realistic Giant Panda dolls. Very few animals in all history have made such a quick "hit" with the public as this black-and-white clown.

The reason, of course, is that the Giant Panda looks as if it had been designed by a toymaker — its black ears, black legs and the black saddle across its back are just the kind of markings an artist might think of for a Christmas toy. Its antics are just as engaging as its appearance, too; young Giant Pandas love to roll and tumble and play.

Scientists have known about the Giant Panda since 1869 when a French missionary sent a skin and some bones of the animal to the Paris Museum, having collected them in a small, mountainous area in western China which is the only place where the Panda is found. Several attempts were made to capture live ones, but they did not succeed until 1937.

Although it looks a great deal like a bear, the Giant Panda is really more closely related to the raccoons. Baby Giant Pandas are born in the winter and are believed to be full grown at about four or five years. An adult may weigh three hundred pounds or more. In China, the Panda eats only bamboo leaves and stems; in captivity it seems to like corn meal mush, too. It is likely to be a dangerous animal when it grows up.

PANDA, LESSER

IT IS HARD for many people to understand why zoologists say the giant panda is more closely related to the raccoon than to the bear, for the giant looks so much more like a bear than like a raccoon. The relationship is easier to see in the case of the Lesser Panda, for with its ringed tail and the dark marks across its eyes it actually reminds one very much of a raccoon.

Both of the pandas live high up in the mountains where the winter cold is intense, and where the thickets of bamboo and the rocky ravines make travel difficult. The Lesser Panda is commoner than the giant. It was discovered a long time before its big cousin, and often has been exhibited.

The Chinese name for the little animal means "Fire-cat," and is an excellent name because its fur is mostly a bright, rusty red. It is like a cat in many ways; it has long, sharp, curved claws and can climb quickly and easily; when it is angry it spits and hisses like a cat; and it likes to sleep curled up like a cat, with its thick tail spread over its body. But its body is about two feet long and its tail eighteen inches long, so it is considerably larger than a cat.

The Lesser Panda is not as particular about its food as the giant panda and eats a variety of fruits, acorns, roots and eggs.

VARIOUS species of Pangolin, or Scaly Anteater, inhabit Africa south of the Sahara, and the Oriental region — India, China, Siam, Indo-China and Malaysia. They are ant- and termite-eaters, and for all practical purposes toothless; they feed by licking up the ants and termites by means of the long, sticky tongue.

The Giant Pangolin of equatorial Africa is about six feet long. It stands only five or six inches off the ground, on sturdy scaled legs, and it moves slowly and deliberately. Frightened, it usually attempts to dig its way underground. Its three- to four-inch foreclaws are useful when the animal attacks the rock-hard termite mounds that are such a common feature of the equatorial forest and the grassy plains. In a few seconds the Giant Pangolin can tear open a termite mound, exposing the honeycomb of galleries filled with soft-bodied termites. Its tongue licks them up as fast as it can flick over the surface. The Giant Pangolin is a ground-dwelling animal, not related to any other animals except the various species of smaller Pangolins.

Some Pangolins are tree-dwellers, feeding on termites that make hard round mud-nests far out on the branches of jungle trees. They are much smaller — fifteen inches to two feet is an average size.

PARADOXURE

THROUGH a large part of tropical Asia and Malaysia there are small animals called Paradoxures that look a good deal like some curious kind of cat. Other names for them are Palm Civets, Palm Cats, Tree Cats or Toddy Cats. The last name "Toddy Cat," is given to them by some people in India because of their liking for palm juice, called "toddy." In this country (where they are often seen in zoological gardens) they are usually called Paradoxures, which is taken from their scientific name, Paradoxurus.

The common Indian Paradoxure is a long and slender animal with a blackish or brownish-gray body almost two feet long, and a tail a foot and a half long. Some of the

Paradoxures have stripes of a darker color on their backs, but others are plain-colored. Paradoxures often carry their tails in a rather tight curl, that makes them look as if the tail *ought* to be prehensile, or grasping. But it is not a grasping tail.

All the Paradoxures are night-roaming creatures, living most of the time in trees and feeding on small birds, small animals and fruits of various sorts. Sometimes they find there is good hunting for food around the native houses and so they "adopt" a native family, and live in the palm-thatched roof, where they hunt rats and lizards and insects.

IN NORTH and South America there is only one animal that can be called a "wild pig." That is the Peccary, which looks a good deal like a pig but which scientists classify in a different family from the wild pigs of Europe and Africa and Asia. We are apt to think of the Peccary as a tropical animal, but the Collared Peccary lives along the Mexican border and is often seen and hunted in southwestern Texas, southeastern New Mexico and southern Arizona. Down there it is called the "Javeline."

The Collared Peccary is found far down into South America, but another kind, called the White-lipped Peccary, also lives in South America and is a little larger and a good deal fiercer. The Collared Peccary is about fifteen inches high; the White-lipped Peccary is around eighteen inches high at the shoulder. Both have bristly, brownish-grayish-blackish hair, and the Collared Peccary is so called because it has a yellowish-white stripe, or collar, around its shoulders.

The Peccaries like sheltered places, such as forests or the mesquite and cactus thickets. They will eat almost anything — fruits and nuts, frogs, snakes, insects and roots. The Collared Peccary travels in small bands and sometimes will "tree" a hunter, for its tusks are sharp and dangerous. The White-lipped Peccary travels in larger bands and is more dangerous, however.

All Peccaries have a strong odor that comes from a gland on the back.

PHALANGER, FLYING

The largest species, the Greater Flying Phalanger, nearly a yard long, has been observed to cover a distance of 590 yards in six successive glides, starting from the top of one tall tree and gliding to the base of another, then climbing high and gliding again.

In contrast to the Greater Flying Phalanger, the Pigmy Phalanger is only about six inches long overall, nearly half of its length being tail.

Some of the Flying Phalangers are related to the Australian 'possums and the cuscus, others (such as the Greater) to the koala. Their babies are extremely small at birth. The Greater apparently has one young at a time, about a quarter of an inch long.

"GLIDERS" or "Flying Squirrels" are names often applied by Australians to the various species of Phalangers found in Australia, New Guinea and the nearby islands. Like the American flying squirrel, they have membranes between the front and hind legs that enable them to glide outward and downward, from tree to tree. They are marsupial, or pouched, animals. All of them feed by night, on fruits or insects or both.

PICHICIAGO

THIS IS a very small armadillo that lives in Argentina. Another name for it is the "Pink Fairy Armadillo," because it is so small and delicate-looking—it is only about five inches long—and because its mantle, or shield covering the top of its body, is pink with long, snowy-white fur underneath.

It seems strange that such a handsome and unusual armadillo should not be known to everybody in the region where it is found, but when a naturalist captured one in 1824 he reported that the natives of Argentina declared they had never seen one before.

However, it may not be so strange after all, for the Pichiciago is an expert digger (like all armadillos) and another naturalist wrote that when he rode up beside one, it started digging in the sandy soil and had buried itself out of sight before he could dismount from his horse and pick it up.

The Pichiciago lives in sandy country, among thorny brushwood and cactus. It comes out of its burrows at night to hunt for ants, termites, snails, worms and vegetable matter.

A kind of Pichiciago slightly larger than the Argentine form lives in Bolivia.

PLATYPUS

A TRULY puzzling animal is the Platypus, or Duckbill, of Australia and Tasmania, for it has fur — but a bill like a duck. It is a true mammal, meaning that its young are fed with milk from the mother's body — and yet it lays eggs!

Some scientists laughed when the first skins of the Platypus were sent to Europe in 1797, and said there "wasn't any such animal." They thought someone had simply sewed a duck's bill onto the furred body of some unfamiliar mammal.

The Platypus lives in and near streams. It digs long tunnels into the bank and here the eggs are laid and the young are hatched. There are usually two eggs, almost round and about three-quarters of an inch long, covered with a soft, parchment-like skin. The babies are very small and are not fully developed when they are hatched, but in about four months they grow to the length of nearly a foot and are able to come out of the burrow and take care of themselves in the water.

A full-grown Platypus is about twenty-two inches long and weighs a little more than four pounds. Its short, soft fur is dark reddish-brown to black and many years ago thousands of the animals were killed for the sake of the pelt, which was made into rugs and capes. Australia now protects the Platypus. The only ones ever exhibited alive outside of Australia came to the Bronx Zoo in 1922 and 1947.

The Platypus eats many kinds of insects, crayfish, earthworms and the like that are found in or near the water.

"PORKY" is one of the best-known animals of our northwoods, for even persons who have never seen one have heard the story that it "shoots" its quills at an enemy. That, of course, is a myth.

The Canada Porcupine is one of our largest rodents, about three feet long and weighing fifteen to twenty pounds when it is in good condition — even thirty to forty pounds when it has been feeding especially well and is fat. Its fairly long, soft hair is slaty-black or brownish-black and is mixed with longer and stiffer hairs and many sharp quills of a yellowish-white color.

When "Porky" is not alarmed, its quills may be pretty well hidden in its fur, but when it "gets its back up" the quills stand out, especially along the lower back. Its thick and muscular tail is well studded with short quills and woe betide the dog or other animal that gets within range, for one slap of the tail will embed the quills in the enemy. These quills have hooks, or barbs, on the tip and keep working into the flesh of the victim.

The Porcupine is an expert climber and is often found in trees. It is fond of salt and comes around camps to gnaw wood, such as shovel handles, that contain salt from sweaty hands. It lives mostly on bark, buds, twigs and other greenstuff. About the only animal (besides man) that goes to the trouble to kill a Porcupine is the fisher.

PORCUPINE, CRESTED

MOST impressive of the rodents known as porcupines is the Crested Porcupine of southern Europe and northern and central Africa. It is heavily armed with quills, some of which are a foot long, and its body size is comparatively large — up to twenty-eight inches exclusive of the short and quilled tail.

When the animal is frightened or angry, the tail shakes rapidly, the whole body vibrates, and the quills stand up in defensive position. The rattling of the quills can be heard many feet away.

Although it is able to climb, it seldom does so, finding most of its food of roots and fruits on the ground.

From two to four young are said to be produced at a birth, in a nest of leaves, grass and roots. The quills of the young are soft when first born, but they quickly harden and even a very young Porcupine is well prepared to defend itself. Few animals, however, dare attack a Porcupine, although hungry leopards and other cat animals sometimes try it, generally retiring with quills in their noses or paws.

The well-quilled Brush-tailed Porcupine of Africa has a somewhat longer, scaly tail that ends in a brush of bristles. None of the Porcupines can "throw" quills.

RELATED to the slow loris of Malaysia is the Potto of Africa — an animal that is even slower in its movements than the slow loris. It is a forest-dwelling, night-feeding animal, generally to be found during the day curled up in a tight ball either in a hollow tree or in some sheltered crotch. The body and tail, the latter about a third of the total length, are approximately fourteen inches long. The soft fur is grizzled honey-colored.

The most peculiar thing about the Potto is the fact that it wears part of its skeleton outside its skin. Several joints of the neck vertebrae have long extensions, or spines, which actually project through the skin as bare, dry bone, for about an eighth of an inch.

The Potto is one of the world's surest-footed climbers as it moves slowly through the trees searching for fruit, leaves and insects. Its hands and feet cling to the branches with a grasp that a man can hardly unloosen. Natives are generally much afraid of the Potto, for they say that if it grasps one's arm, or bites one's hands, it is impossible to get it loose without cutting away the skin. In the forests of the Gold Coast, one of its native names means "The animal that holds tight." Its common name, Potto, comes from another African dialect.

As is the case with many other nocturnal animals, the Potto's eyes are very large, and apparently it can see quite easily in the dusk. It is almost impossible to induce the animal to move about actively in daylight, and even after dark it crawls slowly except when frightened; then it can turn and bite with surprising quickness.

PRAIRIE DOG

THE PRAIRIE DOG is not a dog; it is a sociable, fat, short-tailed ground squirrel that lives in vast colonies called "Prairie Dog towns" on the prairies and great plains of our western and southwestern States.

A full-grown Prairie Dog is about the size of a small woodchuck — fourteen to sixteen inches long, weighing two to three pounds, with short, buff-colored hair that is almost whitish underneath the body.

In the early days of this country there were enormous "towns" of the Prairie Dogs and even today some sizeable colonies exist, although they have been exterminated in many parts of the country by ranchers.

These little animals dig deep burrows with a rim of earth around the edge. They come out early in the morning to enjoy the sun, sitting on the edge of their burrows, and feed on the nearby grass. At the first whistle of alarm, when one of them sees a man or such enemies as a large hawk, coyote, badger and so on, they scurry for shelter in their burrows.

For a long time it was believed that Prairie Dogs, burrowing owls and rattlesnakes all shared the same burrows as friends. That is not true.

PRONGHORN

VERY OLD members of the Kiowa Indian tribe still remember the T'Apk'o Da-agya song of the Antelope Ceremony, for next to the bison, the Pronghorn (or Pronghorn Antelope, as it is often called) was once the commonest game animal in the western United States, and the Indians often had to depend on it for food.

But even Indians must have had trouble getting close enough to a Pronghorn to shoot it, for it is said to be able to run nearly fifty miles an hour for short distances, and the timed speed of one buck Pronghorn was thirty-six miles an hour for twenty-seven miles. Sometimes it is even hard to see the animal, its color of brown and creamy white blending so well into the colors of the wild, broken, desert country that is its home.

When it is frightened, however, it raises a patch of white hairs on its rump and this big white spot, or "flag," can be seen for a considerable distance.

The Pronghorn stands about three feet high, weighs one hundred to one hundred and twenty-five pounds, and both the males and the females have horns which are shed every year. The horns of the females are quite small, however. Although it is called a Pronghorn Antelope, it is not a true antelope; these are found only in Africa and Asia. The Pronghorn eats grasses, weeds, cactus, sagebrush and other low-growing plants.

QUAGGA

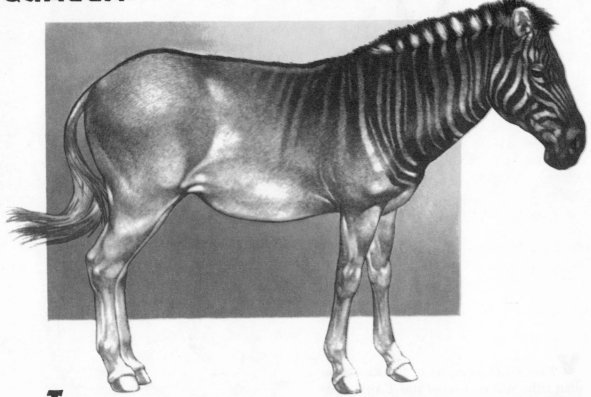

THIS partly-striped animal that is believed to have been related both to the zebra and to the wild ass is now extinct. However, there are many references to it in works on African hunting and exploration, and because of its fairly recent extermination it is included here.

Until the late eighteen-seventies there were still some Quaggas left in South Africa, but now they are all gone. They were killed for food and for the sake of their hides. Early in the last century, however, there were immense numbers of them.

The Quagga was a picturesque animal, strongly striped on the head, neck and fore part of the body but fading out to plain color on the hind quarters. Instead of being black-and-white like the zebra, it was reddish-brown marked with chocolate brown stripes.

The name "Quagga," or "Couagga," as it was sometimes spelled, came from the shrill, barking neigh of the animal.

It is a great pity that such an interesting animal was hunted until the herds grew too small to survive, for it illustrated the relationship between the wild ass (the kiang is an example) and the zebra, being marked somewhat like both of them. It had much more hair on its tail than a zebra, and in this respect was more like a horse.

RABBIT, COTTONTAIL

COTTONTAIL RABBITS of one kind or another are found all over the United States from Canada southward. Not all of them are exactly like the familiar Cottontail of the eastern States (zoologists have named thirty-one species and subspecies) but almost all have the white underside of the tail that gives them the name.

The Eastern Cottontail is about fifteen inches long, with a tail two inches long, and weighs two and one-half to three pounds. Its back and sides are dark brown mixed with gray, and its underparts are whitish.

Millions of Cottontails are killed by hunters each year, but there always seems to be plenty of them. That is perhaps because, in the warmer parts of the country, they pro-duce several litters of young, four to seven at a time. The babies are naked and helpless when they are born in the hollow, fur-lined nest, or form, which the mother builds among tall grass, but within two weeks they are large enough to hop about.

They like rather open, brushy areas in parts of the country where there is such shelter; on the plains, they can be found almost anywhere there are green grasses and plants for them to eat. Unfortunately, Cottontails and human beings like the same kinds of vegetables, and in the country the rabbits often do great damage to early gardens.

RACCOON

THE RACCOON, or "Coon," as it is often called, is so distinctively marked with a black mask across its eyes and a black-ringed tail, that there is no mistaking it. Even if these marks have disappeared when the fur of the animal is turned into Raccoon-skin coats, its grizzled gray-brown-black color is familiar.

The Raccoon is found over most of North America below the lower part of Canada. Sometimes it is a surprisingly large animal — there is one record of a Racoon that weighed forty-nine pounds. The average is a good deal less, however; nearer fifteen pounds, with an over-all length of about thirty inches.

Wherever the Raccoon is common, there is sure to be water, and trees or bushes. It makes its home in hollow trees or logs, usually coming out only at night to feed on anything it can find in and around water. Frogs, fish, birds, snakes, shellfish, insects, acorns and the like are its favorites, but it will eat almost anything. One curious habit it has is washing its food before eating it. Even a frog that has been caught in a stream and is already as clean as a frog can possibly be, will be dabbled in the water again before the Raccoon eats it.

In the northern part of its range, the Raccoon sleeps in a hollow log or tree for about three months during the middle of the winter. Its babies, averaging four, are born in April or May.

IF BRANNICK'S GIANT RAT of South America were as destructive and vicious as it is large, it would be one of the most fearsome animals in the world; it is about two and a half feet in length. Despite its name, it is not closely related to the rats, but is a distant relative of the guineapigs. It looks, indeed, more like a huge, spotted guineapig than anything else. Its hair is black or brown, with two broad white stripes on either side of the middle of the back, and two shorter rows of white spots on the sides.

The home of the Giant Rat is the Andean region of central Colombia through Ecuador to central Peru, then eastward into Bra-zil. It is apparently very rare, and although it was first described by scientists in 1873 it remained almost unknown until 1904. Even now not much is known of its habits, and very few have been seen alive outside its native countries. One reason that it seems rare may be that naturalists simply have not found the area where it is most at home.

Brannick's Giant Rat has a placid, easy-going disposition, and in captivity will allow itself to be stroked without attempting to bite, although it may growl a little. It lives in rocky cliffs or holes in the ground, where it can find protection, and probably hunts its vegetable food mostly at night.

RAT, KANGAROO

A RAT THAT can jump six feet in one leap sounds like a formidable kind of animal, but the Kangaroo Rat is actually a small, delicate and handsome creature quite unlike the animals we think of when the word "rat" is mentioned. Its whole length of eleven inches seems large, but the thin, hair-tipped tail accounts for more than seven of these inches.

The animal has extremely long hind legs and tiny forelegs — thus the name of "Kangaroo" Rat — and its leaps may be only a few inches when it is hopping around looking for food, up to more than six feet when it is frightened. It jumps exactly as if it were on a spring.

The Kangaroo Rat lives in the warmer parts of the West and Southwest, generally in dry, sandy areas. It seems to get along very well without water—its food is mostly dry, such as seeds and grains — and it may not even drink water if it is available.

The short fur of the Kangaroo Rat is reddish-buff on its back and white below. It has fur-lined, outside, cheek pouches where it stores the seeds and grain picked up when it is hunting food.

IN STORIES about the West, one often reads about the Pack Rat, or Trade Rat, which has the habit (sometimes very annoying) of invading a camp at night and carrying off small, bright-colored objects, such as bits of metal, coins, keys and the like. Its name of "Trade Rat" comes from another of its habits—of leaving something (such as a pebble or bits of wood) in the place of the object it has carried away. It is said that on one occasion, a Trade Rat carried away all the rivets in a blacksmith's box, filling up the box with worthless pieces of trash.

Often the objects are carried away to the rat's nest, a jumble of twigs, leaves and debris of various kinds, but they may be tucked away in a crevice in the rocks where they are very hard to find. If it is something that is badly wanted — such as a key to the food locker — the camper may not find the Pack Rat's habits very amusing.

The Pack Rat is almost as large as the common, or Norway rat, with brownish-gray hair above and creamy underparts. It belongs to a large group of attractive and soft-furred rodents usually known as Wood Rats. Its home is in western North America from lower Canada south into Mexico and the Gulf states, with some species ranging up the east coast from Florida.

It feeds on many kinds of green vegetation, fruit, roots, bark, nuts, and so on. Many predatory animals — hawks, owls, snakes, weasels, foxes, coyotes — feed upon it, in turn.

RATEL

"**H**ONEY BADGER" is a name often given to the Ratel of Africa and India because it is somewhat badger-like in appearance and because it has a fondness for sweets, particularly wild honey. Both the Indian and the African Ratels have stoutly-built bodies, lack external ears, and have short legs. The forelegs have comparatively enormous claws which the African species, at least, uses effectively in digging out honeycombs and larval bees from hollow trees. The thick fur apparently prevents the animal from being stung.

While most mammals are light-colored on the underparts of their bodies and darker above, the Ratel is just the reverse, having a grayish back and a black underside. The dark-above-and-light-beneath colora-tion is believed to aid in concealing animals.

Both the Indian and the African Ratels are nocturnal and during the day are generally found sleeping in burrows. They like a wide variety of food, such as rats, birds, frogs, insects and honey; in cultivated districts, they often make raids on poultry roosts.

The Indian species has a bad but probably undeserved reputation as a grave-robber, and is said to disinter corpses in order to feed upon them. What is more likely is that an occasional Ratel wanders into a cemetery and digs there, as elsewhere, for insect larvae.

Illustrative of the animal's liking for sweets is an experience with a captive specimen which was accustomed to a lump of sugar daily. After it grew old and lost its teeth, it learned to soften the sugar in water before eating it.

ALTHOUGH this antelope inhabits grassy or reedy valleys in South Africa, in the neighborhood of water, it seems to have a strong dislike to getting wet and even when it is being pursued vigorously it will go far out of its way to avoid crossing even a little stream. Invariably it will make for dry, bushy country for refuge when it is chased. When a Reedbuck takes shelter from its enemies, it squats almost flat on the ground, "hunched up" like a rabbit.

The Reedbuck is not a particularly distinguished antelope, for it stands only three feet high at the shoulders and its horns are only twelve to sixteen inches long. Only the male has horns. The animal has short, smooth hair that is rather woolly in texture and pale brownish in color. Its tail is short and bushy.

Unlike many antelopes, the Reedbuck seldom travels in large groups and generally only a male, a female and perhaps one or two youngsters are seen together. It eats grass — apparently the only food it takes in the wild.

REINDEER

THE TRUE Reindeer is an Old World animal, but it has many close relatives in the New World — the various kinds of caribou. In recent years, herds of Reindeer have been sent across the Arctic Circle to the Eskimos of Alaska to provide them with meat, transportation and milk. These were, of course, domesticated animals.

The domesticated Reindeer, which serve the Lapps and some other northern people so well, were derived centuries ago from the wild Reindeer, and over countless generations have become slightly different in appearance. Nevertheless, wild and domestic Reindeer interbreed and pure-blooded wild Reindeer are found in comparatively small numbers in Norway and around the Arctic Circle into Asia.

The Reindeer stands about four feet tall at the shoulder and its general color is grayish or drab brown above, buffy whitish beneath. Both males and females carry antlers — an exception to the rule among other members of the deer family that only the males have antlers.

Reindeer find a sparse living among the lichens, frozen grasses and low bush of the northlands. Their greatest enemies are wolves, against which they defend themselves by blows with their forefeet.

RHINOCEROS, AFRICAN BLACK

THE DRY, thorn-bush country of southern and eastern Africa is the home of the two-horned Black Rhinoceros, today greatly reduced in numbers and range. Its body is about ten feet long, its tail twenty-eight inches. Usually, but not invariably, the hind-most of the two horns is the smaller. The record front horn is fifty-three and a half inches long, and was taken from a female.

While it is called the "Black" Rhinoceros, its hide is dark brown rather than a true black; in this respect, its name no more describes it than does the name of the White Rhinoceros, which is merely a slaty gray-black. The White Rhino, found in very small numbers in the Sudan and nearby, is more descriptively called the Square-lipped Rhinoceros. The Black Rhino's lip is hooked rather than squared.

The Black Rhinoceros is a truculent animal. Its sight is poor but its senses of smell and hearing are keen and when it senses danger, it is quite likely to charge rather than to run away. For such a large animal, it is surprisingly light on its feet and is able to wheel and start off in another direction as easily as a polo pony.

Except when annoyed or frightened, the Rhinoceros is harmless and it spends its days browsing on twigs or sleeping in thorn scrub. Somali tribesmen hunt it to make shields of its thick hide.

RHINOCEROS, INDIAN

THERE ARE several kinds of Rhinoce-roses in India, Indo-China and through the Malay Peninsula to Sumatra and Borneo, but the one-horned Indian Rhinoceros is the largest, a big one being more than four-teen feet long and standing as much as six feet four inches at the shoulder. Its single horn is shorter than that of the African black rhinoceros, however, being only about twenty-four inches long. The Sumatran Rhinoceros, which stands some four feet four inches high, is covered thinly with short black hair. Its longest horn is only about nine inches long.

Although the Indian Rhinoceros is pro-tected by law, poachers kill many for the sake of the horn, which is sold to the Chi-nese for medicine for half its weight in gold. Even rhinoceros blood is considered good medicine and is worth $1 a pound dried. In some Eastern countries, people believe that poison becomes harmless if it is drunk out of a cup made of rhinoceros horn and des-potic rulers who are afraid of being poisoned like to have a horn cup handy at meal time.

At one time the Indian Rhino was found all the way from the northwest frontier of India to French Indo-China, but today it is confined to a much smaller area of Nepal Terai, northern Bengal and Assam. It is not a very aggressive animal and like other rhinos, it is a browser, feeding on twigs and grass.

THIS ODD antelope of the cold, flat tree-less steppes of Siberia has the misfortune to be highly prized by the Chinese pharmaceutical trade for the sake of its horns — they bring as much as $250 a pair. Ground into a fine powder, they are used as medicine. Consequently, although the Soviet government makes some attempt to protect the animal, there is a large illegal trade in the horns, and the animal is by no means as plentiful as it was in former days. Only the males have horns.

The Saiga stands about thirty inches high. Apart from its heavily-ridged, amber-colored horns, the most striking thing about it is the large nose. In normal standing pos-ture, the animal's head is bent downward until the nose almost touches the ground. The Mongols of central Asia call it the "Bur-kark," which means "the stooper."

It migrates seasonally, spending the winter in the comparatively snow-free grass-lands in the south of its range and wandering north in early spring as the snow disappears. Its long, thick, whitish winter coat then gives way to summer pelage that is a dull yellowish.

Although adult Saigas can generally escape wolves, young antelopes often fall prey to them. Undoubtedly many Saigas are killed illegally for the sake of their aromatic and tender flesh.

SAPAJOU

SAPAJOU MONKEYS of South America used to be great favorites with organ grinders, for they are gentle and well-behaved if they have been caught young, and they quickly learn to "dance" to the music of the barrel organ and then skip among the crowd to beg for pennies.

"Ring-tail" is another name for this active and excitable little creature, from its habit of carrying its tail over its back, with the end curled into a ring. "Capuchin" is still another name, because the crest of hair on the monkey's head is supposed to look like the cowl of the Capuchin monks.

Almost all zoos have Sapajous of one or more kinds. They are small — hardly as large as a cat — and the fur is generally some shade of brown.

They range over most of South America and some kinds are found in Central America. They travel through the trees in small parties, seeking fruits, insects, birds' eggs and the like. Banana planters do not like them because they may raid a plantation and, being greedy and timid, pull far more fruit from the trees than they can eat.

The Sapajou's tail is prehensile, but it is not as good a grasper as that of the woolly monkey, the spider monkey or the howler, for instance.

THE VOLCANIC island of Guadalupe southwest of San Diego, California, is now the only known home of the great northern Elephant Seal that used to be found all along the California coast but was killed off for the sake of its oil. Its name of "Elephant" Seal comes from its huge nose which looks a little like the trunk of an elephant. Most of the time the nose hangs limply, but when the Elephant Seal wants to look fearsome it can make its nose swell up enormously. Only the male has this tremendous nose, and the female looks very much like an ordinary seal.

The Elephant Seal spends most of its time in the water and can swim rapidly as it hunts for fish and squids, but it comes onto the shore to great rookeries where the babies are born. On land it moves slowly and with a great deal of grunting and puffing and roaring. A big male may be eighteen or possibly even twenty feet long and certainly weighs several thousand pounds — some are said to weigh four tons. The female is only about a third as large.

A seal rookery is a noisy place and each of the animals seems to be trying to roar, bellow or grunt louder than its neighbors. When two males get into a fight, they roar at each other and hurl themselves forward, striking with their short canine teeth. Sometimes they manage to damage each other, but mostly they just make a great deal of noise.

SEAL, FUR

AT ONE time millions of Alaska Fur Seals were killed for the fur trade. Many are still killed each year in the Pribilof Islands where they spend the summer, but the fur is not as popular as it once was.

The big male Fur Seals, that weigh three hundred to five hundred pounds, are the first to arrive at the low, rocky, foggy shores of the Pribilofs. At first they are timid about going on land, but in a few days they take up their stations on shore and when the females arrive some weeks later the males battle fiercely to hold the particular spots of land they have chosen and to induce as many females as possible to join their group. The breeding season extends from May to November, and the female bears one pup.

When the babies are born, the mothers take good care of them, but the males are more concerned with their battles than with the pups, and if a pup wanders away from its mother it stands a good chance of being trampled by fighting males. The babies weigh only three or four pounds and are jet black at first, but after three months this changes to the grayish and brownish colors of the adults.

IN SOME old books of natural history it is said a good way to catch a Harbor Seal is to play sweet music, and that the animal will follow the musician's boat because it loves the tune!

Actually there is a slight amount of truth in the story, for all seals have much curiosity, and the friendly little Harbor Seal might follow a boat just to find out what was making the odd sounds.

The Harbor Seal, or Common Seal, lives along the shores of the North Atlantic and North Pacific oceans. It is not large—about five feet long — and it is so strongly spotted that it is sometimes called the "leopard seal." This name is confusing, however, for the true leopard seal lives in the Antarctic.

In color the Harbor Seal is yellowish-gray with dark brown spots, or sometimes almost black with yellowish spots. Its babies are white when they are born and have a peculiar woolly coat which they shed within a few hours.

The animal is called the "Harbor" Seal because it is usually found around harbors, bays, river-mouths and sheltered sandbars along the coast. It seldom swims far from land, but likes to pitch up and sleep on a rock some distance offshore.

Many stories are told of the friendliness and tameness of the Harbor Seal, which can be trained to follow its owner like a dog.

SEAL, LEOPARD

THE LEOPARD SEAL of the Antarctic seas is truly the leopard of the sea — ten feet long, ashy gray spotted with black, with large, flesh-tearing teeth.

Penguins form a considerable part of the Leopard Seal's diet, although it undoubtedly feeds on other sea birds when it can get them, and on the young of other seals.

This is the only truly predacious seal, for all the other kinds live on fish instead of hunting warm-blooded prey. Millions of years ago before the seals developed as water-dwellers, their ancestors are believed to have been land-dwelling meat-eaters, and the teeth of the Leopard Seal still show that relationship. One part of each molar turns backward, giving the rows the appearance of shark teeth. They are vicious-looking teeth, not mere pegs for holding live fish.

Although the Leopard Seal is a fierce killer of birds, it cannot digest their feathers. One explorer tells of seeing Leopard Seals rolling on the beach, acting as if they had acute indigestion, until finally they disgorged quantities of feathers. Then they went back to the sea.

SEALIONS belong to the seal sub-order but they can be distinguished from the true seals by their external ears and their ability to turn their hind flippers forward and under in order to move about on land.

On land a sealion is awkward when it uses its flippers and its body to "hunch" along, but in the water it has the utmost grace and agility. It needs this great speed in the water, for it feeds largely on fish and has to be swift enough to catch them.

The California Sealion lives from about the middle of California down to the southern end of Lower California. Another kind, called Steller's Sealion, ranges from southern California up to the Bering Sea.

The Sealion is most at home in the sea, but it spends much time on the shore in large colonies called rookeries. Here the babies are born. They have to learn how to swim and how to catch and eat fish, which they do by paddling about in the shallow water and pursuing small fish near shore.

Steller Sealion bulls weigh up to 2000 pounds, and California bulls more than 600 pounds. The cows are only about half as large. When it is wet, a sealion is black and shining; when its short fur is dry it is a rusty brown.

SERVAL

GRACEFULNESS is not a trait of the Serval, for this good-sized, spotted cat of Africa is long-legged and especially so in the forelimbs, so that it seems to be slightly sloping uphill all the time. Its fur is a pale tawny color, with rounded black spots that tend to run together in streaks along the middle of its back. The animal's body is a little more than three feet long and its distinctly ringed tail about a foot long.

Oddly enough, in some parts of Africa (for it is found all over the continent, from Algeria to the Cape, although most commonly in the southern part) there are sometimes all-black specimens. In these, the normally black spots can be seen shining through the black hair.

The Serval seems to have a preference for long grass, reeds and bushes, especially when these are in the neighborhood of small streams or rivers. However, when it is pursued, it does not turn to the water for protection, but climbs a tree.

Its food consists of small animals, such as hares and cane rats, birds and perhaps birds' eggs. Around villages, it is inclined to raid poultry roosts at night. Serval kittens have been reared many times by natives, but they never quite lose their wildness.

THE ROCKY Mountain Sheep is at home in the high, rocky wild parts of the Rocky mountain chain. It is a magnificent animal. The rams are between five and six feet long, stand three and a half feet high at the shoulder, and weigh between two hundred and three hundred pounds. The biggest pair of horns on record was forty-nine inches along the front curve, and since the horns are extremely heavy and broad and curve forward in a graceful line, big game hunters prize them highly as trophies.

It is almost impossible to "sneak up" on a Mountain Sheep, for it is keenly aware of possible danger and its sight and sense of hearing are very sharp. When alarmed, it bounds away over jumbled rocks with surprising speed and ease.

Only the rams have very large horns; the horns of the ewes are quite small. Both rams and ewes are brownish to grayish-brown on the back and yellowish-white underneath; the rams, however, are much darker than the ewes during the breeding season.

The Mountain Sheep feeds on grass, young plants and flowers, or the tender twigs of bushes. Eagles sometimes kill and carry away the lambs.

SHREW

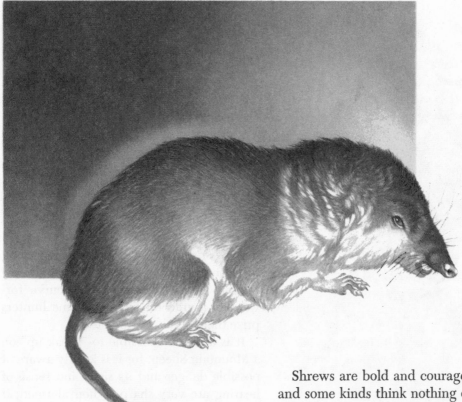

THERE ARE actually dozens of kinds of tiny creatures called Shrews and they are found all over North America, although probably not many people have ever seen them, because they work quietly among the leaves on the forest floor or among fallen and rotting logs where they can find insects and mice. They are among the smallest of all animals and some full-grown Shrews do not weigh more than a penny and the smaller ones have a body that could fit into a large thimble!

Shrews are bold and courageous fighters and some kinds think nothing of tackling a meadow mouse — and killing it and eating it, too. They fight fiercely among themselves. Generally, however, if they have plenty of the insect food they prefer, and sufficiently large living quarters, two Shrews will live together peacefully enough. But they must have plenty of food, for they are said to eat more than their own weight in the course of a day. They will starve to death in a few hours if food is not available.

Shrews have very small eyes and cannot see very well; probably they can only tell light from darkness. They are most active at night.

THE ROCKY Mountain Sheep is at home in the high, rocky wild parts of the Rocky mountain chain. It is a magnificent animal. The rams are between five and six feet long, stand three and a half feet high at the shoulder, and weigh between two hundred and three hundred pounds. The biggest pair of horns on record was forty-nine inches along the front curve, and since the horns are extremely heavy and broad and curve forward in a graceful line, big game hunters prize them highly as trophies.

It is almost impossible to "sneak up" on a Mountain Sheep, for it is keenly aware of possible danger and its sight and sense of hearing are very sharp. When alarmed, it bounds away over jumbled rocks with surprising speed and ease.

Only the rams have very large horns; the horns of the ewes are quite small. Both rams and ewes are brownish to grayish-brown on the back and yellowish-white underneath; the rams, however, are much darker than the ewes during the breeding season.

The Mountain Sheep feeds on grass, young plants and flowers, or the tender twigs of bushes. Eagles sometimes kill and carry away the lambs.

SHREW

THERE ARE actually dozens of kinds of tiny creatures called Shrews and they are found all over North America, although probably not many people have ever seen them, because they work quietly among the leaves on the forest floor or among fallen and rotting logs where they can find insects and mice. They are among the smallest of all animals and some full-grown Shrews do not weigh more than a penny and the smaller ones have a body that could fit into a large thimble!

Shrews are bold and courageous fighters and some kinds think nothing of tackling a meadow mouse — and killing it and eating it, too. They fight fiercely among themselves. Generally, however, if they have plenty of the insect food they prefer, and sufficiently large living quarters, two Shrews will live together peacefully enough. But they must have plenty of food, for they are said to eat more than their own weight in the course of a day. They will starve to death in a few hours if food is not available.

Shrews have very small eyes and cannot see very well; probably they can only tell light from darkness. They are most active at night.

SHREW, MALAYAN TREE

THE TREE SHREWS of southeastern Asia and the East Indies have the distinction of being considered by some zoologists as very distant relatives of man. In late years they have been classified scientifically in the Order Primates that includes man, on the basis of certain structural characteristics. Externally, however, there is nothing man-like about them; they are, in fact, squirrel-like both in their appearance and in tree-dwelling habits.

The Malayan Tree Shrew is six or seven inches long, a rusty brown color, and has a rather long snout. During the dry season it frequents the forests, but is sometimes found around houses during the rainy period of the year. It has a wide distribution from Assam and the eastern Himalayas to Burma and the Malayan islands; in the mountainous regions it is found at elevations up to 6000 feet.

Insects, lizards, and perhaps a certain amount of fruit are the natural food of the Tree Shrew. Little is known about its habits in the wild, and it has rarely been collected alive for exhibition, although apparently it is common enough over a large part of its range.

SITATUNGA

IF THE stories of African natives could be believed, the Sitatunga is one of the most curious of all the antelopes. The natives say it dives into the rivers with the greatest ease and that it will actually go to sleep under the water with only its nose exposed!

However that may be, the Sitatunga is certainly fond of water and can be called "semi-aquatic," for its hooves are so shaped that they enable it to walk through marshy places without sinking in too deeply. This is an adaptation something like that of the camel's big feet which are an aid in walking on sand, or like the spreading hooves of the reindeer that help it in the snow.

The Sitatunga is not a handsome antelope. Its coats is grayish-brown, its horns are about two feet long, and it stands about three and a half feet high at the shoulder.

In the rivers of central, south-central and east Africa, the Sitatunga finds succulent water plants and the shoots of young reeds. If enemies approach while it is feeding, it simply sinks quietly down in the water.

THERE ARE several kinds of Skunks in North America but they can all be recognized by their black-and-white markings, and usually by the odor that follows them. The Large Striped Skunk is found in all parts of the United States, usually around pastures, clearings or in the edges of woods. In the fall it is inclined to travel actively and many Skunks are killed by automobiles.

The Skunk's scent is stored in two glands under its tail. It can be sprayed in a fine mist for a distance of eight or ten feet, so when the animal lifts its tail, puts it head down and taps the ground with its forefeet, it is well to get far away. One "shot" does not exhaust the Skunk's reservoir, either.

A Skunk makes an interesting pet and may live with a family for years without ever discharging its scent. However, it is wise to have the scent glands removed when the animal is still a baby. Any veterinarian can perform the simple operation.

The Skunk is a useful animal, since it feeds on insects, field mice, frogs, snakes and the like. Occasionally, however, it raids a chicken roost and consequently farmers do not like it.

SLOTH

THE SLOTH lives in the great forests of the tropical parts of South America. The one thing that makes it so remarkable, apart from its laziness, is the fact that it spends most of its life upside-down, clinging to the branches of trees. Indeed, it is difficult for it to stand upright or walk on the ground, although it sometimes has to cross the ground to get from one tree to another. It can swim fairly well.

There are Three-toed Sloths and Two-toed Sloths, the names referring to the numbers of the long, curved toes on their front feet. These toes are actually hooks by which the animal clings to the branches as it moves cautiously from one limb to another.

A full-grown Sloth has a body about the size of a large bulldog, and is covered with long, coarse, brownish or ashy-gray hair. An extremely odd thing about this hair is that in the humid jungles it is often coated with a tiny plant, or alga, that makes the Sloth look very much like a part of the mossy trees in which it lives.

The Sloth is most active at night when it is hunting its favorite food, the leaves of the cecropia tree.

SCIENTISTS have known for more than a hundred years that on the islands of Haiti and Cuba there were odd little animals, about the size of guineapigs but with long snouts and long tails, that were called Solenodons. But they had never seen one alive until the early years of this century when an animal collector went to Haiti and distributed hundreds of picture postcards of the Solenodon, made from an artist's drawing of what the animal was supposed to look like. The postcard said the collector wanted to buy one.

Finally a native told him where to look, and he set a box trap and caught several Solenodons. He spent a long time studying the animal, and found that he could trail it through the jungle by the holes it dug and the rotting tree trunks it had pulled apart in its search for ants, grubs, insects, vegetables, snakes and fruit. It searches for food at night and sleeps in the daytime in hollow trees, or holes in the rocks. The Solenodon cannot run very well, for it goes in a zigzag fashion and often trips over its own feet. The natives of Haiti say that when they hunt it with dogs, it is likely to stick its head into a hole, with its body and tail in plain view.

Its relative, the Solenodon of Cuba, is probably extinct now. It was always very rare, and naturalists believe it may have been killed off by the mongoose that runs wild over the island.

SPRINGBOK

THE NAMES of many animals are descriptive of the things they do, and that is the case with the Springbok of South Africa — it has the interesting habit of moving about slowly and serenely, and then suddenly making soaring leaps several feet into the air.

As antelopes go, the Springbok is of only medium size, standing about thirty inches at the shoulder. It is a pretty animal with a pale brown back, a rich brown band on the side, white markings on its face and contrasting white on the rump and lower sides.

It has a warning device, too — a white "flag" of hairs in the middle and rear of its back. These are tucked away in a fold of skin until the animal is frightened or springs into the air, whereupon the fold, or pouch, is turned partly outward and the white hairs stand up as a warning to other members of the herd.

The numbers of Springboks are now far fewer than they were in the last century, when explorers told of seeing great herds of hundreds of thousands on the march to areas where the grass was better for feeding.

EVEN CITY children in the eastern part of the United States are likely to know the Gray Squirrel, for it thrives in parks and usually becomes so tame that it will run up to anyone and beg for a peanut. Naturally, the Squirrel is not as common in a wild forest as it is in a city park where it is fed and protected, but it is found all through the eastern half of the United States, from Canada to Florida. Nor do hunters find the wild Squirrel of the forest as easy to approach as those in the parks; it is extremely shy and wary when it is hunted, and is adept at keeping on the opposite side of the tree from the hunter.

Forest-dwelling Squirrels store up supplies of nuts, fruits, grains and seeds, generally in a hollow tree. They build nests of leaves and twigs in the crotch of a limb, or in hollow trees. Here the babies are born in the spring — from four to six in a litter.

The Gray Squirrel is often playful and delights in racing through the branches and making what seem to be dangerous jumps. But it almost never falls, and if it does fall, is seldom hurt.

SQUIRREL, FLYING

AT DUSK on a warm evening, when crickets and tree frogs and katydids are singing their summer symphonies, the furry little Flying Squirrel awakens, stretches and peers out of the hollow tree where it has slept through the sunny hours. Its big eyes see clearly in the half-light and as it surveys the dark woods it perhaps poises a few moments on the nearest branch to smooth its ruffled, grayish-buff fur. And then, without warning, it hurls itself into space and *glides* toward the earth.

But its destination is another tree, perhaps fifty or more feet away. It skims through the air, all four legs outstretched, and broad, furry tail streaming behind, and as it approaches the distant tree the tail turns as a rudder and the Flying Squirrel swoops upward to land safely and gently against the trunk of the tree.

Then, if it is a nut tree, perhaps a hickory, it runs lightly up the trunk and begins to eat.

The Flying Squirrel in various forms is found all around the world in the northern hemisphere. Those in North America range from rather small creatures hardly larger than a chipmunk to some more northern forms well more than a foot long. All have folds of skin along the side of the body, from the "wrist" of the front leg to the "ankle" of the hind leg, which enable them to glide through the air. They do not, of course, fly by flapping their legs. They are really rather common, but are seldom seen because they are active only at night.

THE CHICKAREE (as the Red Squirrel is often called) is one of our most excitable small animals. When an "enemy" appears, even if it is only a peaceful man wandering through the woods, or a dog in search of a rabbit, the Chickaree mounts its pulpit on the branch of a tree — well out of harm's way — and proceeds to scold, chatter and tell the whole world about it.

Squirrels are found in almost all parts of the globe and the Red Squirrel of North America is one of the smaller kinds, its whole length from nose to end of tail being only about twelve inches. The Red is particularly a forest-dwelling Squirrel and is seldom found outside well-wooded areas. It especially likes evergreen forests and is sometimes called the "Pine Squirrel."

Like many other squirrels, it stores up food supplies of nuts and seeds for winter eating. Very often it fails to go back and dig up its larder and the seeds sprout and grow — which means that the squirrel is a good reforestation agent.

The Red Squirrel has a bad reputation for robbing birds' nests and eating the eggs or the fledglings. In some places it drives out other squirrels from the five to ten acres it considers its own territory.

TAHR, HIMALAYAN

THE HIGHER forested regions of the Himalayas is the home of the Tahr, one of the sure-footed, sturdy wild goats. "Tahr" is a native name and has generally been adopted as the common name in English.

A male stands three feet to three feet four inches at the shoulder; females are slightly smaller. This is a fair size for a wild goat, but the animal is not as impressive as some other wild goats because its reddish-brown hair is quite short about the head and it lacks a beard. Its horns are rather small, too; about twelve to fifteen inches long.

A typical haunt of the Tahr is a tree-covered mountain slope where only a wild goat can travel with ease and security. It is considered a fine game animal because of the difficulty of stalking it in such rough country. Even so, hunters often lose their trophies because the animals fall long distances after being shot.

The Tahr is still plentiful in its mountain fastnesses and has a certain economic value as food for the natives. It is a familiar animal in captivity, for it breeds readily. In the early years of this century one pair was imported into the United States and their descendants now number several hundred animals. Despite the inbreeding, the herd shows no signs of degeneration. Females produce one or two kids, in late spring.

IN THE mountainous regions of Asia there are three kinds of animals known as "goat antelopes" because they resemble both the goats and the antelopes. These are the serow, the goral and the Takin.

The Takin is more or less typical of the group, but is of unusual interest because it is only in rather recent years that much has been learned about it. It is a large animal, standing about three and a half feet at the shoulder, almost seven feet long, and weighing five to six hundred pounds. It lives in the higher parts of the eastern Himalayas, and in the western part of its range its hair is dark gray, but the animals of the eastern areas are much lighter — nearly golden all over. The horns are about twenty inches long.

There is a very good reason why the Takin is comparatively little known; it comes from an extremely rough and difficult country. Its home is between 8000 and 14,000 feet up in the mountains, in dense thickets of rhododendron and dwarf bamboo. The animals trample trails through the thickets and regularly follow them, so that native hunters know where to set traps for them. The Takin spends the daytime in these thickets, coming out at dusk and early in the morning to graze on the grassy slopes. Herds of Takin, led by an old bull, gather around the salt licks in the mountains.

TAMANDUA

ANOTHER name for the Tamandua is the Lesser Anteater and it is a relative of the giant anteater. Both of them live in tropical America.

The Tamandua is only about half the size of its "giant" relative, having a head and body about two feet long and a tail about eighteen inches long. At the front end, the Tamandua and the giant anteater look something alike — both have a long, tapering head and a sticky, whip-like tongue, as well as curved claws on their forefeet. But while the tail of the giant anteater is a tremendous brush of long hairs, that of the Tamandua is slender and short-haired and in fact has no hair at all on the end.

The Tamandua spends a good deal of its life in trees, climbing to the top of even the tallest ones, in search of termites and ants. Its tail is prehensile — grasping — and it can wrap it around a branch and hang on. It is as useful as a hand.

Both the giant anteater and the Tamandua make use of their powerful claws when they are attacked. They will try to escape by running away, but if they are closely pursued they will turn on their enemies and try to hug them in their stout forearms while slashing them with their claws.

THE TAPIR has been described (picturesquely but unscientifically!) as "a pig that started out to be an elephant and then changed its mind."

Tapirs are among the most ancient of living animals. Several kinds are found in South America and Central America, and another in Malaysia far on the other side of the world.

The Giant Tapir, or Baird's Tapir as it is also called, is quite large; a big one may weigh six hundred pounds. It has short, dark brown or blackish hair, and its home is from southern Mexico into Panama. The Hairy Tapir, with blackish hair about an inch long, lives in the high forests from Co-lombia to Ecuador. The other New World Tapir, the Common Tapir, lives further south in South America.

Tapirs are generally forest-dwelling animals, likely to be seen near rivers. They play in the water and love to roll in the mud. A Tapir is rather slow in its movements, shuffling along with its nose close to the ground, and it is not inclined to fight. But if it does attack, it rushes forward and tries to knock its enemy down and bite him.

Tapirs feed on leaves, grasses, water plants, fallen fruits and the like.

TAPIR, MALAYAN

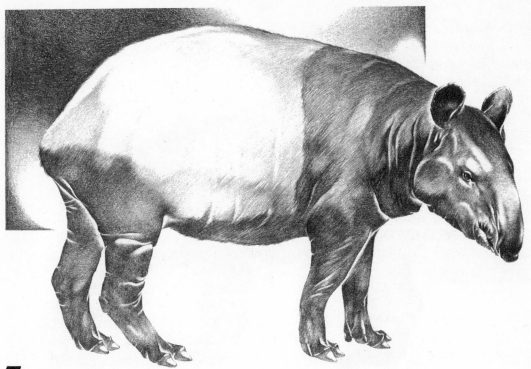

THE JUNGLE people of Siam have a legend about the Malay Tapir: they explain that when God made all the animals, He had some odd pieces of clay left, and so He made the Tapir!

Explorers in the Malay region say that even the natives, who are likely to kill almost any animal for the sake of meat, do not often shoot a Tapir. Its flesh is not very good eating, and it is a shy and inoffensive creature whose chief enemy is the tiger — an animal that is not so particular about what it eats as people are.

The Malay Tapir is the most peculiar-looking of all the Tapirs, for its snout is longer and more elephant-like, and in addition its body is oddly marked — the forepart is brownish-black and so are the hind quarters; the middle of the body is grayish-white. The Malayan species is a rather large Tapir, standing about three feet high at the shoulders — often a little more.

Baby Tapirs are brownish or black, with streaks of brownish-yellow along the sides, so that they look, as someone said, "like little watermelons with four legs."

The Malayan Tapir, as well as those of South and Central America, is a forest-dweller, fond of water and mud in which it wallows very much like a pig. It feeds on water plants, grasses, shoots and buds.

THE WEASEL family (which includes badgers and otters) is a large one scattered all over the world, and in South America there is a large member of the family known as the Tayra. It is about the size of an otter, with a body and tail a yard long (the tail being about half its length), short legs and smooth, dark-brown fur. One distinguishing mark is a light spot on the chest.

The Tayra prefers to do its hunting for food at night, like many members of the weasel family, but it is often still abroad in the morning, and about noon it seeks shelter in its lair for the rest of the day. Its lair may be a deserted armadillo hole or a hollow tree. Being a fierce, dogged fighter, it probably has little trouble running down and killing such small animals as rats and agoutis, and it also hunts birds and robs their nests. Around villages the Tayra has a very bad name because of raids on poultry houses.

Some naturalists report having seen large parties of twenty or more Tayras loping across the prairies in search of food, and one wrote: "When these long-bodied creatures sit up erect, glaring with beady eyes, grinning and chattering at the passer-by, they look like little friars in black robes and gray cowls; but the expression on their round faces is malignant and bloodthirsty beyond anything in nature."

TENREC

THE LARGE island of Madagascar and some small islands nearby are the only places in the world where the Tenrec is found. It is a queer, ancient, long-snouted, insect-eating animal.

In appearance it is somewhat like another insect-eater, the solenodon of Haiti and Cuba — both have long snouts — but the solenodon bears a long, bare tail while the Tenrec has no tail at all. Furthermore, it is considerably larger than the New World animal, with a body about sixteen inches long.

A young Tenrec has a series of rows of spines and stout bristles mixed with the yellowish-brown hair on its back, but as it grows older these tend to disappear and the adult animal has spines only in a kind of collar around the upper part of its neck. These are useful as a defence; when attacked, some kinds of Tenrec roll into a tight ball that bristles with spines.

Even though the natives of Madagascar are fond of eating the Tenrec and dig it out of its burrow when it is hibernating during the colder months, it is not likely that the animal will be exterminated easily, for it has many babies in each litter — from fifteen to twenty-one.

The Tenrec is a strictly nocturnal animal, hunting worms and insects in the low bush country after dark. The long and pointed snout probably is useful in rooting out food of this kind.

THIS IS the largest of the flesh-eating marsupials of the Australian region; it is about the size of a collie dog. Now found only in the wilder and more inaccessible regions of Tasmania, it is often called the Tasmanian Wolf or the Tasmanian Tiger — the latter in reference to the blackish-brown stripes on its back and thighs.

In recent years Thylacines have become extremely rare, partly because of the settlement of the country and perhaps chiefly because the settlers kill it at every opportunity. Wallabies and other small marsupials, rats and birds and perhaps even lizards, are its natural food, but it also preys on sheep and poultry.

It is not a swift animal — not as swift as a dog, for example. But it is tireless in trotting after its victims, and when they are exhausted it rushes forward for the kill; its long canine teeth are somewhat like those of a dog, and it has powerful back molars for crushing bones.

Many observers have noted its habit of rising on its hind legs and leaping kangaroo-like when hard pressed.

The Thylacine is a shy and retiring animal, seldom seen except at dusk when single animals, or pairs, leave the rocky lairs where they have spent the day. It is not dangerous to man unless cornered. Two to four young are born, and are sheltered in the maternal pouch.

TIGER

THE TIGER and the lion are the two biggest members of the cat family and there has been much argument as to which is the more powerful. Experts are inclined to think the Tiger is.

Tigers are found only in Asia, particularly in the jungle areas in India and from northern China to the Malay Peninsula. They are common in Java and Sumatra, but are not found in Ceylon, the Philippines or the Malay Archipelago.

They vary a good deal in size, those living in India and further north being larger than those in Malaysia. A full-grown Bengal Tiger would be ten to twelve feet long, including a tail three to four feet long and would weigh some five hundred pounds.

Tigers kill their prey by leaping at it — they can spring about fifteen feet — and by biting, generally in the throat. They seem to show individual tastes in food; some prefer game such as deer, wild pigs and the like; others feed on cattle, horses, sheep and pigs. A few turn man-eater and are extremely dangerous. Tigers are known to have killed 60,000 head of cattle and 4000 human beings in one year.

Tigers have two to four young in a litter and the babies stay with the family for about two years, after which the young ones are "on their own." They can kill their own small game by the time they are seven months old.

THE COLD and snowy forests of northern Manchuria and southeastern Siberia may seem a strange place to find a Tiger — an animal we usually think of as living in the steaming jungles of the tropics — but that is the home of the huge animal known as the Siberian Tiger. It is rather larger than the better known Bengal tiger — some are said to be thirteen to fourteen feet long — and it is much lighter in color, with thicker, heavier hair.

The Siberian Tiger is gradually being exterminated, as it is hunted for "medicine" for the market in China. Some Chinese believe that tiger's blood and bones are potent medicine, and the beautiful winter coat brings a high price on the fur market, being worth much more than the skins of the short-haired Bengal and other tropical Asiatic tigers.

Like the tigers that live further south, the Siberian Tiger customarily feeds on wild game but occasionally individuals become man-eaters, often because they have been wounded and can no longer bring down fleet game. Many years ago work had to be halted on the Chinese Eastern Railway until Cossacks could exterminate the tigers that were killing the workmen.

UAKARI

IN THE great jungles of central South America there are various small monkeys called Uakaris, with long, silky hair and short, stumpy tails. One, the Bald Uakari, has a bright scarlet face and its body is clothed in almost white hair.

In the jungle along the Amazon River, troops of Uakari Monkeys live and travel together through the trees. They are good climbers but not very good jumpers, and prefer to run along nimbly from bough to bough. Mother Uakaris carry their babies on their backs as they run through the branches. The natives say that these little monkeys (they are only about eighteen inches long) spend all their lives in the trees and never willingly come down to the ground. They live on fruits and there is plenty to eat in the thick, matted tops of the jungle trees.

The Bald Uakari seldom becomes tame in captivity. Natives often capture the animals, sometimes by shooting them with blow-gun darts dipped in a weak poison, but they say the monkeys remain sulky and peevish and would rather bite than make friends. Probably it all depends on making a pet of the monkey when it is very young.

LIKE ITS relative the guanaco, the Vicuna is an ancient member of the camel family whose ancestors wandered into South America millions of years ago. It is about one-fourth smaller than the guanaco; it stands about two feet nine inches high at the shoulder.

Small herds of ten to fifteen females and an adult male are to be found in the mountains of Peru, above the forest line. Individuals become tame quite easily and ranchers often keep one or two animals around as pets, or fence in a herd and shear it for the sake of the wool. In the early days, Indians used to round up a herd, drive it into a funnel-shaped natural corral among the rocks and take the wool. Afterwards they turned the animals loose. Actual domestication of the Vicuna as a wool-growing animal is not practicable because each animal yields only about a pound of wool, and most of the Vicuna wool of commerce comes from animals that have been killed. The fleece is a creamy light brown.

Since 1920 Peru has forbidden the making of goods from Vicuna wool and Bolivia, also, has prohibited the export of wool and skins. As a result, the herds are no longer in immediate danger of extermination.

At the high altitudes where they live, Vicunas have few natural enemies but they are subject to many parasites, especially at lower altitudes.

WALLABY

THE NAME "Wallaby" is given to some of the smaller and more brightly-colored kangaroos of Australia. They vary a great deal in size, from the big Red-necked Wallaby whose body is about forty inches long and whose tail is some thirty inches long, to other members of the group that are scarcely larger than rabbits. Many of the Wallabies live in scrub brush country and for that reason are also called "Brush Kangaroos" instead of Wallabies. Others, known as Rock Wallabies, are dwellers in rocky regions. They are astonishingly sure-footed as they leap among the stones.

Wallabies are good jumpers, almost as good as the large true kangaroos — and, like the kangaroos, they feed on grass and vege-tables and roots. When they are feeding they move about on all four feet, but when they are resting or looking around they stand up and support themselves on their enormous hind legs and tail.

Wallabies and kangaroos generally travel in groups that may number fifty or more. These groups are called "mobs." Wallaby and kangaroo babies are called "Joeys" by the people of Australia.

After the Joeys leave their mothers' pouch, five or six months after they are born, they gather in little "mobs" of their own. But a Wallaby Joey, like the Joeys of the larger kangaroos, is a lazy little creature and stays with its mother as long as it is small enough to get back in her pouch.

ONE LARGE member of the kangaroo family that lives in the mountain country of eastern Australia is known as the Wallaroo. It is a stout and heavy kangaroo with rather long and thick smoky-gray fur.

Like all kangaroos, it is a marsupial. Its babies are only about an inch when they are born and spend the next several months in a pouch or fold of skin on the mother's abdomen, where they develop. The babies are hairless when they are born and do not look very much like kangaroos — in fact, their front legs are longer than their hind legs at birth. When they grow up, of course, the front legs are quite tiny while the hind legs are extremely large and powerful.

Wallaroos and other members of the family are vegetarians, feeding on roots, grasses and vegetables. They are not afraid of water and are said to be able to kill dogs that attack them by grasping the animals with their forefeet and holding them under the surface until they drown. But unless a Wallaro is attacked, it is ordinarily a very peaceful animal.

The Wallaroo fights with its hind feet, rearing back as if it were sitting on its tail and then kicking forward with its feet. These have large claws and can inflict painful injuries.

WALRUS

THE NAME "Walrus" comes from a Scandinavian word, *valross*, meaning "whale-horse" and the connection — at least as far as the whale is concerned — is easy to see, for a big male Walrus may weigh as much as a ton and a half and be ten to eleven feet long.

Walruses are found in the Arctic seas of both the Atlantic and the Pacific Oceans. They are sociable animals and those in a given neighborhood are likely to be found together, on or near the shore or among masses of floating ice. One naturalist who cruised among a herd of Walruses which had not learned to fear man, reported that they followed his boat for long distances, swimming alongside and raising themselves out of the water in order to see these strange visitors. Others found "grandstand seats" on ice floes and loaded the cakes of ice so heavily that they sank beneath the surface.

The body of the Walrus is wrinkled and almost hairless, dark brown in color. Both males and females have very long upper canine teeth, or tusks, about fifteen inches long. These they use for grubbing up clams and other molluscs from the bottom, as hooks for dragging their heavy bodies over land, and in fighting. They crush such food as clams in their flat teeth, swallow the soft parts and reject the shells.

Even Walrus babies have long, bristly whiskers that make them look like grizzled old men.

THIS IS the large deer (the largest in North America next to the Moose) that most people call the "Elk," because of a mistake by early settlers who thought it was like the European Elk. "Wapiti" is supposed to be a Shawnee Indian name for the animal.

At one time the Wapiti was found over most of North America from lower Canada to as far south as Pennsylvania, and westward to the Rockies. Now it has disappeared in the East, and is still found wild only in the Rocky Mountain region and far western states.

Bull Wapiti are much larger than the cows, or females, and stand about five feet high at the shoulder, weighing seven hundred to one thousand pounds. An adult cow would weigh about five to six hundred pounds. The bulls have truly magnificent antlers; a record head had a spread of five feet. During the summer Wapiti scatter and feed on grass, leaves, twigs, and small plants high in the mountains, but they come down to the more sheltered valleys and lowlands in the winter.

In the fall, when the animals are mating, the big bulls challenge each other with a snorting call or "bugle." Sometimes, in their fierce fights, their antlers become interlocked and cannot be separated; when this happens, both animals struggle until they are exhausted and die.

WARTHOG

THE WARTHOG has the reputation of being the ugliest animal in the world. Everything about it seems ridiculous and exaggerated, from its huge, curling upper tusks which are so blunt and so backward-curved that they are almost useless as weapons to its slender little tail that ends in a ravel of hair. Its "face" looks more like a shovel than a hog's snout, is decorated with a pair of knobs that give the animal its name of "wart" hog, and its pores usually exude a good deal of oil so that it always seems to be in need of a bath.

Most Warthogs have a pleasant disposition, although they can fight efficiently with their sharp lower tusks and many a lion has learned to his sorrow that a Warthog is not such easy prey as it looks.

The Warthog lives in the plains region of Africa, for unlike all other pigs it is never found in thick forests. It is a better grazer than most pigs but it also roots up the earth, getting down on its knees to plough into soil with its lower tusks.

It lives in burrows and when a Warthog is pursued it will run for its burrow at headlong speed (up to thirty miles an hour), with its little tail held straight and high. Just as it reaches its hole in the earth, it whirls around and goes into the burrow backward, so that its tusks are facing outward ready to meet the enemy.

THE WATERBUCKS are fair-sized antelopes of the grassy plains region of Africa south of the Sahara. The native name of "Defassa" in Abyssinia is sometimes used as a common name in English; so is the name "Sing-Sing," used by the natives of Gambia. The Common Waterbuck of eastern Africa is slightly smaller than the animals of the Defassa group. It stands about four feet high. The horns of some subspecies reach a length of a yard, but the average is around twenty-five inches.

Although they are animals of the plains in an equatorial region of great heat, the

Waterbucks have long coats of reddish-brown hair.

They are water-loving rather than water-dwelling antelopes, always to be found feeding and resting on dry land among the low bush and clumps of trees. When alarmed, however, they usually make for the nearest water, either a stream or a papyrus marsh. Hunters say that they will come to bay in a pool or stream, if pursued by dogs, and take to water even if there are crocodiles in sight.

All the Waterbucks are highly polygamous and an old bull will collect a harem of a dozen to twenty cows. Sooner or later the young bulls are driven away by the old master, until the time comes when his powers fail and then a sturdy young bull takes over the herd.

WEASEL

VARIOUS species of the small, slender, slinking Weasels are found all around the world, mostly in the northern hemisphere. Those of North America range even into the Arctic Circle, and seem formed by Nature to fit into every type of habitat. The smallest is the Least Weasel, in northern Canada, only six inches long; the largest, the Black-footed Ferret, which preys upon prairie dogs, is twenty-three inches long. Various names are applied to the Weasels, such as Ermine, Stoat and Ferret.

Almost everywhere the Weasels have a bad reputation — largely undeserved — as ruthless killers of poultry. Weasels undoubtedly do raid a poultry house, killing chickens and drinking their blood and often killing more than is necessary for their food requirements. But for one such "rogue," there are vast numbers that have never tasted chicken-blood, and serve the farmer well as destroyers of injurious rodents.

The Weasels in cold climates change color, from summer brown to winter white, at the beginning of the winter; the old hair falls out and is replaced by new. Young are born in litters of four to eight.

THE LARGEST animal in the world is the Whale, and the largest of the many kinds of Whales is the Sulphur-bottom or Blue Whale, that is known to reach a length of 103 feet and an estimated weight of 147 tons! Even a baby Blue Whale is a "whopper" — about twenty-three feet long at birth. The Blue is said to be the fastest swimmer of all the Whales; its speed when alarmed has been estimated as nearly twenty miles an hour.

Although Whales live only in the ocean (the Blue Whale is found both in the Atlantic and in the Pacific, from the Arctic to the Antarctic) they are *not* fishes, but are true mammals.

Immense numbers of Whales have been killed by the whaling industry in the last century and a half, but nevertheless not very much is known about their habits, food, reproduction and so on, for whalers seldom kept records except of the number of barrels of oil obtained from each Whale.

The Sperm Whale, now rather scarce, although it is found in all seas, is famous for producing an intestinal secretion known as ambergris, a yellow-brown substance which is sometimes found on the seashore. It is used as a base for perfumes, and is very valuable.

Whales breathe air, like other mammals, and while they can descend to considerable depths in the ocean, they must come to the surface to breathe. It is when they have come up and are expelling their breath, blowing a column of air and water for several feet in the air, that they are said to be "spouting."

WISENT

PROBABLY there are few, if any, pure-blooded Wisents left alive in the world. The Wisent is (or was) the European Bison and although hundreds of years ago it was common all over Europe, it was killed off as civilization spread and the forests were cut down, until there were known to be only a few dozen of them in the forests of Lithuania in the nineteen-thirties. These were probably exterminated during the World War II. Some remained in European zoos but it is uncertain whether all of them are pure-blooded.

The Wisent is not as handsome an animal as its close relative, the American bison, being taller in its forequarters (a little more than six feet tall at the shoulders), with a smaller head and a smaller hump. Its thick hair is brown with a touch of plum color.

As late as 1914 there were only about 700 Wisents left in Lithuania and perhaps even fewer of the Caucasian race of the animals in the Caucasus Mountains. The latter are now extinct and there are not believed to be any left, even in European zoos. For many years wild life protection organizations have tried to preserve the remaining Lithuanian Wisents, but political changes in various countries made it difficult.

Unlike the American bison, which was a plains-dwelling animal, the Wisent lives in the thick woods, feeding on leaves, twigs and bark.

EXCEPT for a few breeds of domestic dogs, the Wolves are the largest members of a family that also includes the dogs and jackals. They are found all around the world north of the Equator, and the most familiar kinds are probably the Gray Wolf of North America that used to prey on the great bison herds, and the European Wolf that, in so many stories and legends, was a terror to human beings in the mountainous and forested regions of Europe. The Gray and the European Wolves are considered by some zoologists to be the same species.

The Gray Wolf once ranged over all of temperate and Arctic North America except a dry, hot area in the southwest, but it has been exterminated over most of this country by the increase of farms and cities.

A few wary animals survive in the West and there are a good many in the far North. They like rough, rocky country and open plains.

The Gray Wolf weighs seventy-five to one hundred pounds; the females are smaller and weigh sixty to eighty pounds. Both are gray sprinkled with black; sometimes they are rusty red.

The European Wolf is slightly taller and lankier. It hunts its prey (any kind of smaller animal, or even larger creatures, and livestock) in small packs. Wolves are not dangerous to human beings except under unusual circumstances — as, for instance, if they should be famished with hunger. Generally their only idea is to avoid meeting men.

WOLVERINE

ZOOLOGISTS classify the Wolverine as a member of the weasel family; indeed, it is the largest of the group. But it looks very little like the smaller and more familiar creatures in that family. The Wolverine is about three and a half feet long and weighs up to thirty-five pounds.

Another name for the Wolverine is "Glutton," which means, of course, someone who eats far more than he ought to. Actually, the Wolverine does not seem to be any more gluttonous than many other animals, which are likely to eat all they can hold when food is plentiful.

The Wolverine used to live from the Arctic ocean south through Canada and the northern United States even down to Maryland, but it has disappeared from all parts of the United States except the northern borders. It is rare even in Canada.

It is a fierce fighter and extremely strong; a Wolverine in capitivity once tore apart a heavy wire mesh cage and escaped, although the cage was supposed to be strong enough to hold a medium-sized bear. In the wild, the Wolverine sometimes attacks and kills deer and caribou, although usually it feeds on smaller animals and even on mice and grasshoppers. It is said to kill big animals by climbing a tree and dropping on the neck of its prey. Hunters hate the Wolverine because it robs their traps.

THE WOMBATS of Australia and Tasmania are reminiscent, in appearance and habits, of the American woodchuck. Their remote ancestors were probably tree-dwellers, but the Wombats of today are ground-living burrowers and eaters of grass, the inner bark of certain trees, roots and occasionally of fungus. They are marsupials, or pouched, animals.

The smallest, the Island Wombat, weighs twenty-five to thirty pounds, and the large Common Wombat reaches a length of three feet nine inches and a weight of eighty pounds. Some species inhabit forest-covered hills, others more level and open coastal country.

All are fast diggers and are described as lying on their sides to dig, kicking the loosened soil out with their feet. Nesting burrows vary greatly in length but some have been explored that were a hundred feet long, with a bark-filled nest at the end. In one tunnel, perhaps an old one made by an unusually large animal, the diameter was so great that a child could have crawled the entire distance through it.

Ordinarily the Wombat feeds only at night, but it may come out during the day for a sunbath in a shallow excavation a few yards from the entrance to its burrow.

The single young is born between April and June and is carried in the female's pouch until the end of the year, by which time it is fully furred. Wombats are solitary animals except in the mating season, and are harmless to man. Their "voice" is a hoarse, growling cough.

WOODCHUCK

THE LARGE, ground-dwelling member of the squirrel family that is known variously as Woodchuck, Groundhog or Marmot, is found over most of the United States and in the west as far north as Alaska.

The grizzled grayish-brown 'Chuck is one of the most familiar mammals in the eastern states, often seen placidly cropping grass and clover alongside the express highways and paying no attention to automobile traffic. Its more usual habitat is hilly farmland, where it burrows in clay banks and clover fields or makes a home in stone walls and woodpiles. Clover and garden produce are two of its favorite foods, and where Woodchucks are plentiful, country gardening is difficult. Farm boys generally kill Woodchucks on sight. Although seldom eaten, they are really excellent.

After feeding all summer, the Woodchuck is very fat in early autumn and its coat is thick and glossy. When winter comes, the 'Chuck goes underground to hibernate. It may weigh eleven to thirteen pounds at this season, but the fat disappears during the winter and when the Woodchuck emerges in March it may weigh only seven pounds. The young, two to five in number, are born in the spring in a grass-lined burrow several feet underground.

There is no truth in the story that if the Groundhog sees its shadow on February 2, there will be six more weeks of winter weather.

ON THE great, bleak plateau of Tibet where the winter temperature drops far below zero and where the land is too inhospitable even for human beings with their knowledge of shelter and fire, the wild Yak is perfectly at home. Indeed, it can stand the bitter cold far more easily than it can the heat of more southerly climes.

One reason is perhaps the tremendous coat of hair that it wears; its back and sides are liberally covered with coarse black hair which blankets the lower part of its body in a mantle that almost sweeps the ground.

The wild Yak — which is really a kind of wild cattle — roams up to 20,000 feet. Most of the year the old bulls wander separately or in twos and threes, while the cows and calves stay together in much larger herds providing protection against wolves.

It feeds upon the coarse grasses of the region. Because of its immense strength and long horns — there are records of horns nearly forty inches long — it is safe from most enemies except man and his guns.

The Yak has been domesticated and used as a beast of burden for a long time. Its strength and endurance are almost unbelievable and an explorer has told of struggling through deep snow for six hours, with heavily laden Yaks, during which time the animals climbed and fought their way through the snow without complaint. One even rolled down a mountainside, shook itself, and climbed back up.

YAPOK

THE YAPOK is a South American Water Opossum, with normal hands and great, webbed feet. It is the most beautiful of all the opossums. About the size of a muskrat, with a tail longer than its body, it is vividly marked with velvety black blotches on a background of silky gray and creamy white fur.

Although it is found over a great part of northern South America, always in thick forests near jungle pools and streams, it is believed to be very rare — at least, it is rarely seen.

No doubt this is partly because it is nocturnal and is adept at hiding under water or in a hole in the bank when frightened.

It digs burrows three or four feet long in the river banks, well above the water line and often under overhanging roots. In these burrows the young are born in December or January. There are said to be from five to nine babies.

The Yapok remains in its burrow during the day, for the light seems to hurt its eyes. At dusk it comes out to feed on crayfish, small fish, water insects and perhaps on water plants. The shells of crayfish it piles up in little mounds outside its burrow. It builds "pillows" of dry leaves along the bank and rests on these, scurrying for the nearest hole at the first sign of danger.

"THE HORSE with the tiger's stripes," as the Zebra has been called, is one of the best-known of African animals, for almost all zoos and circuses exhibit it. Although it is frequently bad-tempered and dangerous, it lives well in captivity.

The home of the Zebra is on the grassy plains of Africa south of the Sahara Desert, for it is a grazing animal. There are a number of kinds of Zebras, which are chiefly different in the arrangement of their stripes. The Grevy Zebra, for instance, has narrow, close-set black stripes all over its white body. Grant's Zebra has much broader stripes, and the Mountain Zebra has rather narrow stripes on the fore part of its body and broad, widely-spaced ones on its flanks and hind legs.

Zebras generally travel in small herds, but sometimes in quite large ones, or may even travel with a party of gnus as if for companionship or mutual protection. The lion is the Zebra's worst enemy, although if the Zebra sees the lion in time, a few well-aimed kicks may rout it.

If it is caught young and carefully trained, a Zebra can occasionally be broken to harness — as when a circus exhibits a pair of Zebras pulling a cart. But it is not trustworthy and trainers and keepers have to be on the alert all the time.

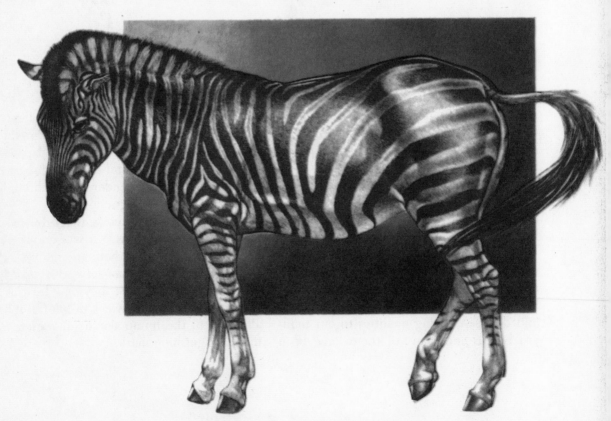

ZEBU

ZEBUS, or Brahman Cattle, often called the sacred cattle of India, are not really wild animals, for they have been domesticated for at least 6000 years and no truly wild members of the species are known. They are a curious, hump-backed cattle, gentle in disposition and well-adapted to domesticaion.

It is believed that the Zebu is among the ancestors of the modern breeds of cattle, although nobody really knows. Nevertheless, the Zebu is still used to give hardiness and disease-resisting qualities to our modern breeds and many of them have been imported into the United States and into South America for that purpose. The Hindus of India hold the hump-backed cattle in religious esteem and certain favorite bulls are allowed to wander at will through the bazaars in the villages.

According to one theory, the Zebu may have originated in Africa; it was known in ancient Egypt. Today there are many varieties and colors — some have one hump, others have two humps; they may be gray, creamy, reddish or brownish in color. But in all of them the hump on the shoulders is the distinguishing mark.